ChefV.®

MAKING HEALTHIER EASIER

MAKING
CLEANSING
EASIER

Healthy, Delicious, Naturally-Cleansing Recipes from Chef and Nutritional Therapist

VERONICA WHEAT

Photos by Mike Pawlenty

CHEF V. ORGANIC GREEN DRINK AND CLEANSE
MADE LOCAL. DELIVERED FRESH.
CHEFV.COM 866.709.6060

© 2016 Chefs Press, Inc., San Diego, California
www.chefspress.com

Text copyright © Veronica Wheat
Photos copyright © Mike Pawlenty

President + Publisher: Amy Stirnkorb
Executive Vice President: Mike Pawlenty
Design + Production: Amy Stirnkorb
Editing: Margaret King
Food Pyramid Graphic: Karen Floyd

FIRST EDITION
ISBN: 978-1-939664-03-7
Printed in China

*I dedicate this book to all of my
awesome Chef V employees and customers.
My sincerest thanks to everyone who works so hard
at Chef V, helping to make us what we are today
and hope to become in the future — and to
everyone who supports Chef V,
I am truly grateful.*

INSIDE

WELCOME TO MAKING CLEANSING EASIER

Every person deserves a healthy body and a healthy life. Throughout my life I have made it my goal to help as many people as possible lead healthier and happier lives, from the nutritious foods I prepare to the green drinks, smoothies, and cleanses I've created.

In this book, I will show you how to prepare healthful meals and snacks using organic, nutrient-rich foods that are cleanse-approved and good for your body. But don't think that means boring or bland. These recipes are delicious and look amazing, too. I have created recipes that are both healthy and tasty — using fresh, raw ingredients, a wide variety of herbs and spices, and gluten-free, dairy-free foods that are loaded with flavor. Trust me, eating my way will be fun! And I promise, you won't miss your old food.

I won't be giving you a quick fix. It will take time, and it will take some work, but you can get the healthy life you deserve, and I want to help you achieve it!

But being healthy is more than simply eating healthy. It means being physically active and finding new ways to exercise. Besides being a chef, I am also a certified nutritional therapist and yoga instructor. I prefer to start my day with exercise and drinking 8 ounces of water every hour in between meals to stay hydrated, feel full, and flush out toxins. We have all become so sedentary, sitting at our desks, staring at our computers and our smartphones. Our bodies were built to move. So now is the perfect time to commit to a daily exercise routine — try 30 minutes of fast-paced walking, light yoga, or even tennis lessons.

It is my hope that by sharing my story and recipes I can guide you and help your new healthy lifestyle take root!

HOW IT ALL STARTED

For almost as long as I can remember, I have been passionate about cooking and nutrition. I grew up in Palm Desert, California, and as a teenager one of my favorite things to do was to hit the kitchen and whip up healthy dinners for my family. I naturally gravitated to jobs in restaurants, and when I was 18, I fell in love with yoga, and eventually became a certified yoga instructor. Yoga, along with my passion for nutritious foods, is what led to my balanced, healthy lifestyle.

In 2008, I moved to San Diego and began studying psychology at California State University San Marcos. Living in Southern California is fantastic for me because of the emphasis on health and fitness — and, of course, the abundance of fresh local produce. Here I discovered the farmers markets, which make gorgeous local and organic produce readily available.

I have always loved cooking and educating people about the benefits of a healthy lifestyle, but it didn't occur to me that I could turn my passion into a career. Instead, I was thinking about going on to graduate school — and frankly, I was dreading it. Then one day, my fiancé, Brandon, asked me, "If you could do anything without worrying about money, what would you do?"

Without hesitation, I answered, "I would cook! Hands down!" He looked at me and said, "Well, what are you waiting for?"

So I followed my passion and started creating and delivering healthy meals to customers weekly. Each delivery also included my own special organic green drink, made from locally sourced greens, with instructions to have a glass before every meal. Well, the green drink really struck a chord. Clients shared it with friends. Word got around about the benefits people were experiencing. Everywhere I went, people asked me, "Hey, Chef V, how can I get your green drink?" I would tell them, "You have to sign up for the meal plan." But more and more people kept telling me they just really wanted my green drink. Eventually the demand became so great that I stopped making meals and began concentrating on getting my green drink to as many people as possible.

ORGANIC — THE FOUNDATION OF A HEALTHY LIFESTYLE

My company, Chef V, is a certified organic brand, something I am very proud of. Not only do my kitchen and production processes exceed the rigorous National Organic Program, everything we produce is made using locally grown organic produce and organic ingredients.

As a nutritional therapist, I am always looking for ways to educate people about healthy living and the role that organics should play in our lives. To illustrate the importance of organics as the basis of a healthy diet, I developed my own organic food pyramid (see page 12), detailing from top to bottom which organic foods we should eat and how much of each we should consume each day.

I strongly believe that we need to put the best organic foods into our bodies in order to get the best out of ourselves. Start with fresh, organic, local foods. Know where your food comes from, how it's grown, how it's raised. It's always my first question and it should be yours too.

When you buy organic, it means that the entire operation is protecting natural resources, maintaining biodiversity, and using the safest approved, non-genetically modified (non-GMO) ingredients.

When you buy local, you know that you're getting the freshest, tastiest, and most nutrient-rich foods. Local foods also promote a safer food supply by reducing the opportunities for contamination during packing, storing, and shipping the food from its source to you.

Nearly every community has access to seasonal farmers markets and many now have a Whole Foods, Trader Joe's, or other local organic specialty or natural food store. But when you consider that Costco, that mega big box store, has become the United States' largest organic grocer, there's no excuse for not making fresh, organic whole foods the basis of your new healthy life.

GREEN IS GOOD

Dark leafy green vegetables — including collards, dandelion greens, parsley, chard, green leaf lettuce, and all types of kale — are nutritional powerhouses for many reasons. They contain an abundance of phytonutrients and carotenoids — antioxidants that protect cells and play a key role in fighting and preventing diseases, including cancer and heart disease. They also have high levels of iron, magnesium, potassium, calcium, and other important vitamins and minerals. Dark leafy greens are great for achieving and maintaining a healthy body weight thanks to being high in fiber, which keeps you feeling full and helps keep your blood sugar levels from spiking, leading to a more controlled appetite.

So when I started my meal delivery service, I began making a green drink as an extra — and super easy — way for my customers to get more greens in their diets every day. Introducing all of these health benefits into your system doesn't require anything more than starting each day with a big glass of green drink before you eat your breakfast.

In creating the green drink, I went through a lot of trial and error, but finally I landed on the perfect combination of seven nutrient-packed organic greens — black kale, green kale, curly parsley, collard greens, dandelion greens, green chard, and green-leaf lettuce — with a little fresh, organic apple thrown in for flavor.

You have undoubtedly seen the lineup of commercially prepared green drinks in your grocery store, but you should know that not all green drinks are created equal. Most are pasteurized or processed in a way that destroys nutrients. What makes my organic green drink special? It's raw, and it's made in small batches from the freshest locally sourced organic greens. While some drinks are prepared by juicing, mine is cold-blended, so you get the complete package of nutrients and fibers from these fresh, whole ingredients. Many green drinks are mostly fruit with a few veggies thrown in. But that means they are full of sugar — which we know is bad for our bodies. Because my drink is nearly all veggies with just a tiny bit of fruit, it's really low in sugar. Other green drinks may have 30 grams of sugar in an 8-ounce serving, but mine has only 3 grams!

When it comes to my organic green drink, I definitely practice what I preach — I enjoy it almost every day. It has become such an important part of my life that I worry about missing it when I travel. The most beneficial way to consume it is to have it in the morning on an empty stomach. This changes my whole day. I probably drink close to a half gallon a day — just like water. Whenever my body is craving something, I give it my organic green drink first, then listen to my body and see what it really wants. Sometimes when I think I'm hungry, I have a little green drink and voilà! I wasn't really hungry, I just needed some greens.

As you take these steps, you will be amazed at how much better you will feel and how your taste buds will begin to change and enjoy eating fresh, clean foods.

TIME TO CLEANSE

Just as important as adding fresh greens to your life is ridding your body of all the bad stuff you've been pumping into it particularly those highly processed foods, alcohol, caffeine, sugar, and pollutants. Manufacturers have added so many artificial substances, and so much sodium, fat, and sugar to their pre-packaged and canned foods to try to make them palatable, but in the end, these things just harm our bodies. Many doctors believe, as do I, that there is a cancer-sugar connection, and it really is in your body's best interest to rein in your sweet tooth.

One of the best ways to flush the toxins out of your system and begin to revitalize your body is to cleanse, but not everyone should dive head first into one. I've had clients who've said: "I'm going to the drive-thru tonight, and then I'm starting my cleanse tomorrow." But that's a recipe for failure. People who start this way often wind up feeling sick during the cleanse and may even give up on it. Their bodies are full of toxins, so of course they feel bad.

What I've learned is that you should pre-cleanse first — to ease your body into the detoxification process and begin to open up your channels of elimination, especially the liver and colon. This is achieved through a period of healthful eating, and to make it easier for you, I have compiled a chart of cleanse-approved foods (see page 14). You should stick to these foods for at least two days before you begin my organic cleanse. If you're used to having a lot of sugar, coffee, or alcohol, you may need to take three to five days. For continued success, stick to these cleanse-approved foods for two days or more after your cleanse.

The purpose of the cleanse is restore your body to its optimal health, and pre-cleansing will help you have a more pleasant cleanse experience and achieve longer-lasting results. Once the detox process starts, all the toxins in your body dislodge from the various tissues where they have been hiding, and now, thanks to the pre-cleanse, your liver and colon are better prepared to eliminate these as swiftly and efficiently as possible.

If you are under medical care or on prescription medications, always consult with your doctor first before cleansing. Note that any over-the-counter medications, alcohol, tobacco, or illegal drugs will increase your toxic load and your cleansing process may not be as effective.

When you sign up for one of my Organic Cleanses, you will receive pre-cleanse instructions the week before you begin to get you started as well detailed instructions for each day of the cleanse. My Cleanses include my green drink, protein shakes, and a special detox soup — all delivered right to your door — and will help you lose weight, rev up your energy levels, and feel better than you ever thought possible.

A NEW NORMAL — CHEF V ROUTINE

Once you've completed a cleanse, you may think it's time to jump right back into your old routines. "OK, I'm done. Let's order a large pizza, and I'm going to pig out." But that's undoing all the hard work you've just done, and it's tough on your body. So, to transition out of the cleanse and to maximize its benefits, you need to stick to my list of cleanse-approved foods for two to five days — and while you're doing this, really reflect on how good you feel.

Think twice before you start reaching for unhealthful foods again — now is the perfect time to create your new normal.

My goal with my Chef V Green Drinks and Cleanses has always been about helping others feel better, and now with this book, I can do even more. I want you to become the healthiest YOU possible. I think you want it too or you wouldn't be here, now, reading my book.

On the following pages, I will show you how to make delicious and satisfying meals that treat your body right. As a chef, I love cooking and eating flavorful healthy foods, and I want you to do the same. I've created recipes for everything from appetizers to desserts made entirely from cleanse-approved ingredients. These dishes are so yummy, you will not feel deprived but will think you are indulging big-time.

Ultimately, my message to you is this: Achieving true wellness begins with creating a new, healthy lifestyle where there wasn't one. There is no quick fix. There is only a journey to be enjoyed and relished as you begin to see and feel the new you emerging — the results of being committed to yourself, your mind, and your body. It's about eating right, drinking lots of water, and exercising.

You don't have to be perfect all the time. Maybe you're going out to dinner or to a special event and you know you will be eating some less-than-ideal foods. Don't beat yourself up over an occasional indulgence. Just keep some consistency in your diet and your exercise routine. Make sure you are giving your body good things most of the time. You will see how alive and full of energy you feel. I hope my green drink, cleanses, recipes, and advice will help you get there.

Yours in good health. *Bon Appetit!*

Chef V

CHEF V'S KITCHEN ADVICE

I love lists. They help me stay organized and make grocery shopping so much easier. This list includes ingredients (and my favorite brands) that I use for many of my recipes, so you will want to always have these items on hand. Try to use the freshest organically grown, humanely raised, and sustainably sourced products. I also share with you my favorite kitchen tools. In addition to the recipes in this book, you can find others at ChefVblog.com.

MY MUST-HAVE PRODUCTS AND FAVORITE BRANDS:

- Cold-pressed organic olive oil — Bragg® is a great brand and is very affordable.
- Cooking spray — Trader Joe's® Coconut Oil Spray
- Raw unfiltered organic apple cider vinegar — Bragg®
- Organic stocks and broths — Superior Touch® Organic Better Than Bouillon
- Organic sea salt — I like to use Himalayan Pink Salt; any organic brand is fine.
- Raw unsweetened nut milks — Chef V's Raw Almond Milk, see recipe page 32; Trader Joe's® unsweetened almond milk, or any organic unsweetened brand.
- Raw coconut nectar is a natural liquid sweetener. It's the sap from coconut palm blossoms and is low-glycemic and does not cause a spike in blood sugar. It does not taste like coconut; it has a rich, sweet taste, and so it can be used in a variety of ways — in drinks, desserts, or anywhere else you need a sugar substitute. My favorite brand is Coconut Secret.®
- Raw coconut aminos is an organic coconut sap aged and blended with sun-dried mineral-rich sea salt. It is a terrific soy sauce replacement. My favorite brand is Coconut Secret.®
- Coconut milk — For most cooking, including soups, and making desserts I like Thai Kitchen,® but for smoothies and cold dishes like cereal, I prefer Trader Joe's® or Whole Foods® Refrigerated Unsweetened Coconut Milk.
- Gluten-free bread — Udi's,® Veganic,® or any other brand that is vegan and gluten-free.
- Gluten free flour — Bob's Red Mill® Gluten-Free All-Purpose Flour
- Brown rice pasta — Trader Joe's® or Tolerant® Red Lentil or Black Bean Pasta
- Tri-color quinoa — Trader Joe's® Organic Qunioa
- Raw unsalted nuts — Whole Foods® organic nuts
- Raw sprouted seeds — Go Raw® Sprouted Sunflower Seeds
- Dried organic spices — Cumin, red pepper flakes, cayenne pepper, and turmeric; any organic brand is fine.
- Plus these fresh organic ingredients: Ginger, turmeric, lemons, and herbs

MY GO-TO KITCHEN GADGETS:

Vitamix, cheesecloth, garlic press, good-quality chef's knife and paring knife, wooden spoons, zip-top bags for storing cleaned veggies, non-stick skillet, large stockpot, saucepans, and sauté pans.

CHEF V'S
ORGANIC FOOD PYRAMID

As a nutritional therapist and chef, I am always looking for better ways to communicate my message about healthy eating. So I remade the outdated USDA Food Pyramid and created my own Organic Food Pyramid to illustrate what to eat. For maximum nutrient absorption and ease of digestion, I recommend eating foods with the most vitamins and nutritional value first. Follow my food pyramid every day, eating foods mostly from the bottom and less from the top. As part of your healthy lifestyle, always drink 8 (8-ounce) glasses of filtered water every day. For more on healthy eating, turn to pages 14-17, where you will find my Cleanse-Approved Food Chart, which details and explains why each item is recommended or should be consumed in moderation.

WHAT TO EAT AND EATING ORDER

1. Dark Leafy Greens: Green kale, black kale, collard greens, green chard, rainbow chard, dandelion greens, parsley, green leaf lettuce, spinach, mustard greens, turnip greens, beet greens, mesclun, romaine, red leaf lettuce, endive, and sorrel. These greens are rich in vitamins, minerals, anti-cancer phytonutrients, and essential for your diet. This is why I separated them from other organic vegetables.

2. Vegetables: Broccoli, Brussels sprouts, cabbage, cauliflower, bok choy, beets, carrots, radishes, parsnips, burdock taproot, yams, sprouts, kelp, wakame, Irish moss, spirulina, chlorella, nori, dulse, basil, rosemary, thyme, parsley, dill, cilantro, dandelion, clover, onion, shallots, scallions, leek, chive, garlic, fennel, carrots, mushrooms, ginger, turmeric, cumin, black pepper, cinnamon, and oregano.

3. Fruits: Avocado, cucumber, apple, pineapple, watermelon, cantaloupe, mango, blueberries, blackberries, raspberries, green beans, snap peas, snow peas, English peas, zucchini, summer squash, butternut squash, and pumpkin.

4. Legumes: Split peas, black beans, kidney beans, pinto beans, lentils, lima beans, white beans, black-eyed peas, chickpeas, and asparagus beans.

5. Nuts and Seeds: Always choose raw unsalted almonds, walnuts, pistachios, pine nuts, sunflower seeds, pumpkin seeds, sesame seeds, chia seeds, hemp, and flaxseeds.

6. Animal Protein: Fresh or water-packed cold-water fish including trout, salmon, halibut, tuna, mackerel, sardines, pike, kippers, flounder, and haddock; wild game including rabbit, pheasant, bison, venison, elk; organic lamb, duck, chicken, and turkey.

7. Grains: Quinoa, brown rice, red rice, black rice, wild rice, millet, amaranth, teff, tapioca flour, and buckwheat.

8. Healthy Fats: Raw, cold-pressed avocado oil, coconut oil, and olive oil.

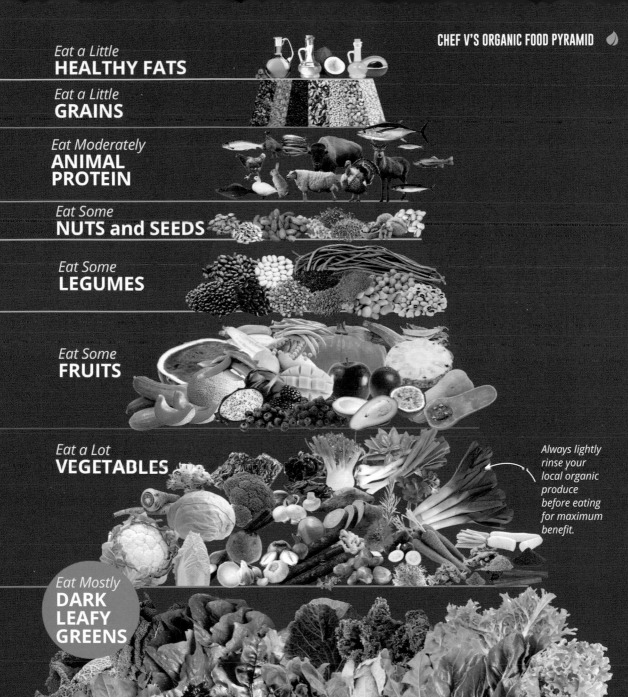

Eat a Little
HEALTHY FATS

Eat a Little
GRAINS

Eat Moderately
ANIMAL PROTEIN

Eat Some
NUTS and SEEDS

Eat Some
LEGUMES

Eat Some
FRUITS

Eat a Lot
VEGETABLES

Always lightly rinse your local organic produce before eating for maximum benefit.

Eat Mostly
DARK LEAFY GREENS

CHEF V'S CLEANSE-APPROVED FOODS

I have thoroughly researched each of the items on my cleanse-approved food list on the following pages. I list and explain why each is recommended or should be consumed in moderation. For more on healthy eating, you can find my Organic Food Pyramid and detailed listing of all the acceptable foods to eat on pages 12-13.

PRODUCT	OK	IN MODERATION	WHY / WHY NOT
Alcohol	None	Beer, wine, hard liquor	Stressful to the detox organs and can cause a multitude of metabolism and other health issues. Beer and hard liquor contain gluten. Wine contains sulfites. Both gluten and sulfites are common allergens. High in sugar.
Beverages	Filtered water, green, white or herbal tea, coconut water, Chef V's Green Drink, kombucha	Soft drinks, coffee, seltzer or mineral water	Caffeinated drinks are highly acidic, dehydrating, and stressful to the detox organs they create surges of adrenaline and cause nervousness and disrupt natural rhythms in the body (sleep, hormones, etc.). Regular and diet sodas contain corn syrup, sugar or artificial sweeteners, caffeine, have zero nutritional value, are highly processed, and research indicates that diet sodas actually increase appetite and promote weight gain.
Breath mints, candy, chewing gum	None	None	Full of sugar and artificial sweeteners.
Chocolate	Raw cacao nibs or powder	Processed cocoa and chocolate	Chocolate is full of dairy and sugar, and roasted and processed cocoa does not have the health benefits that raw chocolate or cacao does.
Condiments	White or apple cider vinegar; all spices; all herbs; sea salt and Himalayan salt; black pepper; stone-ground mustard and those without added sugar or dyes; miso; raw coconut aminos; wheat-free tamari; wheat-free nama shoyu; unsweetened whole fruit jam	Balsamic vinegar, ketchup, relish, chutney, traditional soy sauce, barbecue sauce, teriyaki sauce, all processed condiments	Use salts in moderation. Table salt is heavily processed, with beneficial minerals removed. Balsamic vinegar is higher in sugars than other vinegars. Ketchup contains tomatoes and is full of high fructose corn syrup. Tomatoes are part of the nightshade family of vegetables and are high in alkaloids, can be mildly toxic, and are believed to increase inflammation and decrease digestion in the body. Traditional soy and teriyaki sauces are processed and full of sodium.

PRODUCT	OK	IN MODERATION	WHY / WHY NOT
Dairy, dairy substitutes	Hemp, rice, and nut milks, coconut milk, nut cheeses, Daiya®	Cow, goat, sheep milk and cheeses, cottage cheese, heavy cream, yogurt, ice cream, non-dairy creamers, butter, ghee	Dairy products are often contaminated with toxic mold. A major allergen, highly mucus-forming, and acidic to the body. Pasteurized yogurt has had all its healthful properties destroyed and often contains sugar or artificial sweeteners. Ice cream has all the negative properties of dairy. Avoid even non-dairy ice cream during the cleanse.
Eggs	None	From pasture-raised, free-range, organic chickens	Major food allergen.
Fruits	Unsweetened fresh or frozen whole fruits, fresh-squeezed, unsweetened fruit juices, lemons, limes	Bananas, strawberries, grapes, oranges, grapefruits; nightshades, including tomatoes, sweet peppers, eggplant	Bananas are full of starch and sugars. Strawberries and grapes are common allergens and are fruits likely to be covered with pesticides and herbicides, even those labeled organic. Many citrus fruits have a high potential for an allergic response. Grapefruits may block certain enzyme processes in the body. Lemons and limes are alkalizing and detoxifying and are good for your body. Nightshades are often high in alkaloids, can be mildly toxic, and are believed to increase inflammation and decrease digestion in the body.
Grains, gluten	None	All wheat: Kamut khorasan, spelt, einkorn, farro/emmer, barley, rye, triticale	Major food allergen. Often contaminated with toxic mold. Also avoid processed vegetarian/vegan food such as seitan, tempeh, and textured-vegetable protein (TVP).
Grains, non-gluten	Quinoa, brown rice, red rice, black rice, wild rice, millet, amaranth, teff, tapioca flour, buckwheat	Oats, field corn, white rice	Oats can often be contaminated with gluten grains. Corn is a common allergen, often genetically modified, and contaminated with toxic mold. White rice can spike blood sugar and can contribute to insulin resistance, raising the risk of developing Type 2 diabetes.
Juices, commercially bottled and fresh-pressed	Chef V's Green Drink	Cold-pressed or high pressure pasteurized juices	Are generally pasteurized, reducing or destroying the available vitamins and nutrients. Concentrated fruit juices (including fresh-squeezed or pressed) are high in sugar and can cause significant spikes in blood sugar.
Legumes	Split peas, lentils, black beans, lima beans, chickpeas **** See pages 12-13 for complete list**	Peanuts, peanut butter	Are a high-protein source of vitamins, minerals, antioxidant compounds, and dietary fiber except for peanuts. Peanuts are a major allergen. Non-organic peanuts are laden with chemicals, and both organic and nonorganic peanuts are often contaminated with toxic mold.

PRODUCT	OK	IN MODERATION	WHY / WHY NOT
Tree nuts	Raw, unsalted almonds, brazil nuts, cashews, hazelnuts, macadamia nuts, pecans, pistachios, pine nuts, walnuts, nut butters		In general, raw nuts are preferred because their fats have not been damaged by heat processing. If you soak nuts in water for a few hours or overnight, the fat content is cut by as much as half. Soaking also breaks down the enzyme inhibitors present in the skin of raw nuts so the nutrients and proteins can be accessed.
Soybeans, soy-based products	None	Soybeans, edamame, soymilk, soy ice cream, soy sauce, tofu, soybean oil, tofu, tempeh, miso	Major food allergen. Often contaminated with toxic mold. Be aware of soybean oil in processed foods.
Meat	Chicken, turkey, rabbit; lean wild meat such as buffalo, duck, ostrich, pheasant, venison; lamb	Beef, pork; any processed, cured, or smoked meats such as lunch meats or hot dogs.	Always choose organic, hormone/antibiotic-free, grass- or pasture-fed, lean meats. Red meat is acidic to the body, highly stressful to all organs, especially the detox organs (liver and kidneys). Animals raised for meat are often given hormones and antibiotics that are very harmful to humans. Grain-fed animals have much less protein, and their fats are not as healthy.
Oils, fats	Cold-pressed olive oil, flax, safflower, sesame, almond, avocado, sunflower, walnut, pumpkin, and coconut oils	Butter, margarine, shortening, processed oils and partially hydrogenated oils, commercially produced salad dressings,	Use all oils in moderation. Avoid oils that are refined or not cold-pressed. Margarine is made mainly of refined vegetable oil and water, but may also contain milk or animal fats. It is highly processed. Canola, cottonseed, peanut, and hydrogenated oils must be avoided because they trigger free radicals in the body.
Seafood	Fresh or water-packed, cold-water fish such as trout, salmon, halibut, tuna, mackerel, sardines, pike, kippers, flounder, haddock	African butterfish, billfish, bluefish, carp, catfish, dorado, eel, hilsa, mahi-mahi, monkfish, pomfret, sturgeon, shark, skate, snakehead, swordfish, tilapia, tilefish	Cold water, fatty fish provide more heart-healthy fish oils and lower risk of parasites and containments than warm water, lake, or farm-raised fish. Some fish farms take extra precautions to limit contaminant exposure, but it may be best to choose wild or wild-caught fish when possible. Wild-caught fish are born in a hatchery, then released into the wild and caught once they reach adulthood.
Seafood, raw	Seared fish	Sushi	Avoid the raw forms of all meat and seafood due to the high risk of parasites.

PRODUCT	OK	IN MODERATION	WHY / WHY NOT
Seafood, shellfish	None	Abalone, barnacles, chiton mollusks, clams, cockles, crab, crayfish, cuttlefish, geoduck, lobster, mussels, octopus, oysters, prawn, scallops, sea cucumbers, shrimp, sea snails, squid, sea urchins	High risk of parasites and heavy-metal contamination. Farm-raised fish and shellfish can contain higher levels of contaminants than wild or wild-caught fish. Some fish farms take extra precautions to limit contaminant exposure, but it may be best to choose wild or wild-caught fish when possible. Wild-caught fish are born in a hatchery, then released into the wild and caught once they reach adulthood.
Seeds	Raw unsalted seeds, seed butters ** *See pages 12-13 for complete list*		Great source of dietary fiber and healthy fats
Sweeteners	Stevia, coconut nectar, coconut sugar, yacón syrup, whole fresh fruit, date paste	Refined sugar, all white and brown sugars, maple syrup, molasses, high-fructose corn syrup, regular and evaporated cane juice, concentrated fruit juice, agave nectar, brown rice syrup, all artificial sweeteners Splenda,® Equal,® Sweet'N Low,® dried fruit	Use all sweeteners in moderation. Aspartame is an artificial sweetener and a definite toxin with many side effects, including brain damage and inflammation. Saccharin is believed to be a carcinogen and also leads to carbohydrate cravings. Splenda® is a chlorocarbon that causes swelling of the liver and kidneys and shrinking of the thymus gland, along with other negative side effects. Sweet'N Low,® Equal,® and other artificial sweeteners are chemicals and toxic to the body. They provide a false sense of energy without any nutrients, which can lead to a blood sugar crash, food cravings, weight gain, and other unpleasant side effects.
Tobacco, nicotine, e-cigarettes + other drugs	None	None	Even so-called organic tobacco, which is free of added chemicals and pesticides, causes inflammation in the lungs and arteries, disrupts natural blood-sugar levels, and stresses the adrenal glands and the heart. And no matter how you deliver it to your body, nicotine is one of the most addictive substances on earth.
Vegetables	Raw, preferably fresh, steamed, sautéed, juiced, or roasted vegetables, spirulina, chorella ** *See pages 12-13 for complete list*	Creamed vegetables, corn, nightshades including potatoes	Nightshades are often high in alkaloids, can be mildly toxic, and are believed to increase inflammation and decrease digestion in the body. While some spices are in the nightshade family, dried peppers such as cayenne, chile pepper, and paprika, and fresh chile peppers such as jalapeños, habaneros are allowed in cooking because they have detoxifying properties, and in general, very small amounts are used. Corn is a common allergen, often genetically modified, and contaminated with toxic mold. High in starch and sugar, it has a high glycemic index and will raise blood sugar faster, causing insulin levels to spike.

what the symbols mean:
vegan • raw • paleo • dairy-free
gluten-free • kid friendly

V R P DF GF KF

CHEF V'S
DETOX DRINKS + SMOOTHIES

I recommend blending, not juicing, to retain all the nutrient-rich fibers in your fruits and vegetables. The vitamins and minerals in a blended beverage help you boost your metabolism, burn fat, feel more energized, sleep better, and eat healthier. Start your day off right like I do with a Chef V's Green Drink every morning or make your own detox drinks and smoothies. For even more nutrition, stir in a tablespoon or two of flaxseeds or chia seeds. And always try to use the freshest organically grown, humanely raised, and sustainably sourced ingredients.

Chef V's Tip: Want to get more calcium into your diet? Look no further! My Berry Blast is chock full of calcium from sources you may not know — almonds (from my raw almond milk), chia seeds, and flaxseeds. Calcium is essential for a healthy heart, bones, blood, and more.

BERRY BLAST
SERVES 1

1 cup Chef V's Raw Almond Milk
   (See recipe, page 32) **or coconut milk**
½ Fuji apple, cored and seeded
½ cup fresh or frozen raspberries
½ cup fresh or frozen blueberries
1 teaspoon raw chia seeds
1 teaspoon raw flaxseeds
1 cup ice
1 tablespoon vegan protein powder,
   optional

Process all ingredients in a Vitamix for 1 to 2 minutes, or until smooth. Will keep for up to 3 days refrigerated.

V R P DF GF KF

LEMON GINGER DETOX

SERVES 1

½ lemon, juiced
¼ teaspoon grated fresh ginger
¼ teaspoon ground turmeric
1½ cups cold or hot filtered water

Mix lemon juice, fresh ginger, and turmeric with either cold or hot water, and serve. This is a great drink to start your morning and also for an afternoon lemonade. Follow it with a low-sugar green drink for the best detoxifying results in the morning. Will keep for up to 3 days refrigerated.

V   R   P   DF   GF

Chef V's Tip: Lemon and ginger detoxify the liver and strengthen the immune system.

Chef V's Tip: Watermelons are a good source of thiamin, potassium, and magnesium, which protect our body from many diseases. Also rich in vitamins A and C.

WATERMELON SLUSH
SERVES 1

1 cup chilled seedless watermelon pieces
1 cup cold filtered water
1 cup ice

Process all ingredients in a Vitamix for 1 to 2 minutes, or until smooth. Will keep for up to 3 days refrigerated.

V R P DF GF KF

Chef V's Tip: Mangos contain tartaric acid, malic acid, and a trace of citric acid, which help maintain the alkaline balance of our bodies.

TROPICAL GREEN DRINK
SERVES 2

¾ cup fresh or frozen mango pieces
½ cup fresh or frozen pineapple pieces
2 large green kale leaves
1 large green chard leaf
2 cups cold filtered water
½ cup ice

Process all ingredients in a Vitamix for 1 to 2 minutes, or until smooth. Will keep for up to 3 days refrigerated.

V R P DF GF KF

CREAMY GREEN SMOOTHIE
SERVES 1-2

1 small ripe avocado
2 large leaves green kale
1 cup spinach
2 medjool dates, pitted
1 lemon, juice only
Pinch cinnamon
1 tablespoon chia seeds
1½ cups filtered water
1 cup ice

Process all ingredients in a Vitamix for 1 to 2 minutes, or until smooth. Will keep for up to 3 days refrigerated.

V R P DF GF KF

Chef V's Tip:
Go red! Research has
shown that red fruits
and vegetables such as
beets and raspberries are
nutritional superheroes.
So drink up!

BEET-IT SMOOTHIE
SERVES 1

½ cup fresh or frozen blueberries
½ cup fresh or frozen raspberries
¼ cup red beet, peeled and chopped
1 leaf red chard
1 cup Chef V's Raw Almond Milk
(See recipe, page 32)
½ cup ice
1 tablespoon vegan protein powder, optional

Process all ingredients in a Vitamix for 1 to 2
minutes, or until smooth. Will keep for up to 3 days
refrigerated. **V R P DF GF**

Chef V's Tip: Kale is a wonder in the world of super foods. It is packed with carotenoids and flavonoids, the key antioxidants that protect our cells from free radicals.

GREEN PROTEIN SMOOTHIE
SERVES 1- 2

2 large leaves green kale
1 medium leaf green chard
½ cup fresh or frozen mango pieces
½ cup fresh or frozen pineapple pieces
1 cup ice
1 cup Chef V's Raw Almond Milk *(See recipe, page 32)*
1 scoop plain or vanilla vegan protein powder (use hemp, pea, or brown rice protein; do not use soy protein)

Process all ingredients in a Vitamix for 1 to 2 minutes, or until smooth. Will keep for up to 3 days refrigerated.

(V) (R) (P) (DF) (GF) (KF)

Chef V's Tip: Carrots are packed with beta-carotene, potassium, and other vitamins and minerals that benefit our eyes, skin, digestive system, and even our teeth.

CARROT BLEND
SERVES 1-2

2 medium-sized carrots
½ Fuji apple, cored and seeded
1 lemon, juice only
1 tablespoon grated fresh ginger
2 cups cold filtered water
1 cup ice

Process all ingredients in a Vitamix for
1 to 2 minutes, or until smooth. Will keep
for up to 3 days refrigerated.

Chef V's Tip: This smoothie not only tastes great but is loaded with antioxidants that fight free radicals and reduce inflammation.

GINGER APPLE BERRY SMOOTHIE
SERVES 1-2

½ Fuji apple, cored and seeded
½ cup fresh or frozen blueberries
½ cup fresh or frozen raspberries
2 small leaves red chard
1 tablespoon grated fresh ginger
¾ cup Chef V's Raw Almond Milk
   (See recipe, page 32)
1 cup ice
1 tablespoon vegan protein powder, optional

Process all ingredients in a Vitamix for 1 to 2 minutes, or until smooth. Will keep for up to 3 days refrigerated.

V R P DF GF KF

Chef V's Tip: Both ginger and turmeric are two powerful spices that have anti-inflammatory properties and aid digestion and liver cleansing.

HOT DETOX TEA

SERVES 1

8-12 ounces boiling water
1 bag non-caffeinated tea
⅛ teaspoon ground cinnamon
⅛ teaspoon fresh or ground turmeric
⅛ teaspoon fresh or ground ginger
⅛ teaspoon apple cider vinegar
1 lemon wedge
1 cinnamon stick, optional

Steep tea for 3 minutes. Add spices, vinegar, and a squeeze of the lemon wedge. Enjoy warm!

V P DF GF

what the symbols mean:
vegan · raw · paleo · dairy-free
gluten-free · kid friendly

CHEF V'S
HEALTHY BREAKFAST OR ANYTIME IDEAS

Starting your day off right is essential. My routine begins with drinking water first thing when I get up to help stimulate my colon. Drink water all day long; I drink 8 ounces every hour in between meals to keep hydrated, feeling full, and to flush out toxins. I also prefer to exercise in the morning, always on an empty stomach, to boost my metabolism and burn stored fats. The best workouts are light and consistent, so you'll do them again the next day. Try 30 minutes of light yoga or a fast-paced walk. Next, I have my Green Drink and wait 15 minutes before having one of my healthy breakfast ideas.

EASY CEREAL WITH CHEF V'S RAW ALMOND MILK

SERVES 1

Chef V's Tip: My Raw Almond Milk is easy to make and so versatile; I use it throughout this book. Or, an ice cold glass of it is refreshing on a hot summer day.

CHEF V'S RAW ALMOND MILK

3 cups raw almonds
3 cups filtered water

CEREAL

½ cup Chef V's Raw Almond Milk or coconut milk
¼ cup crushed raw almonds
¼ cup crushed raw walnuts
¼ cup fresh blueberries
1 tablespoon unsweetened shredded coconut

To make the almond milk, process 3 cups of raw almonds and 3 cups filtered water in a Vitamix until liquefied. Strain through a cheesecloth into a mason jar and seal. Will keep for up to 3-5 days refrigerated.

To make the cereal, combine all the ingredients in a bowl and serve.

V R P DF GF KF

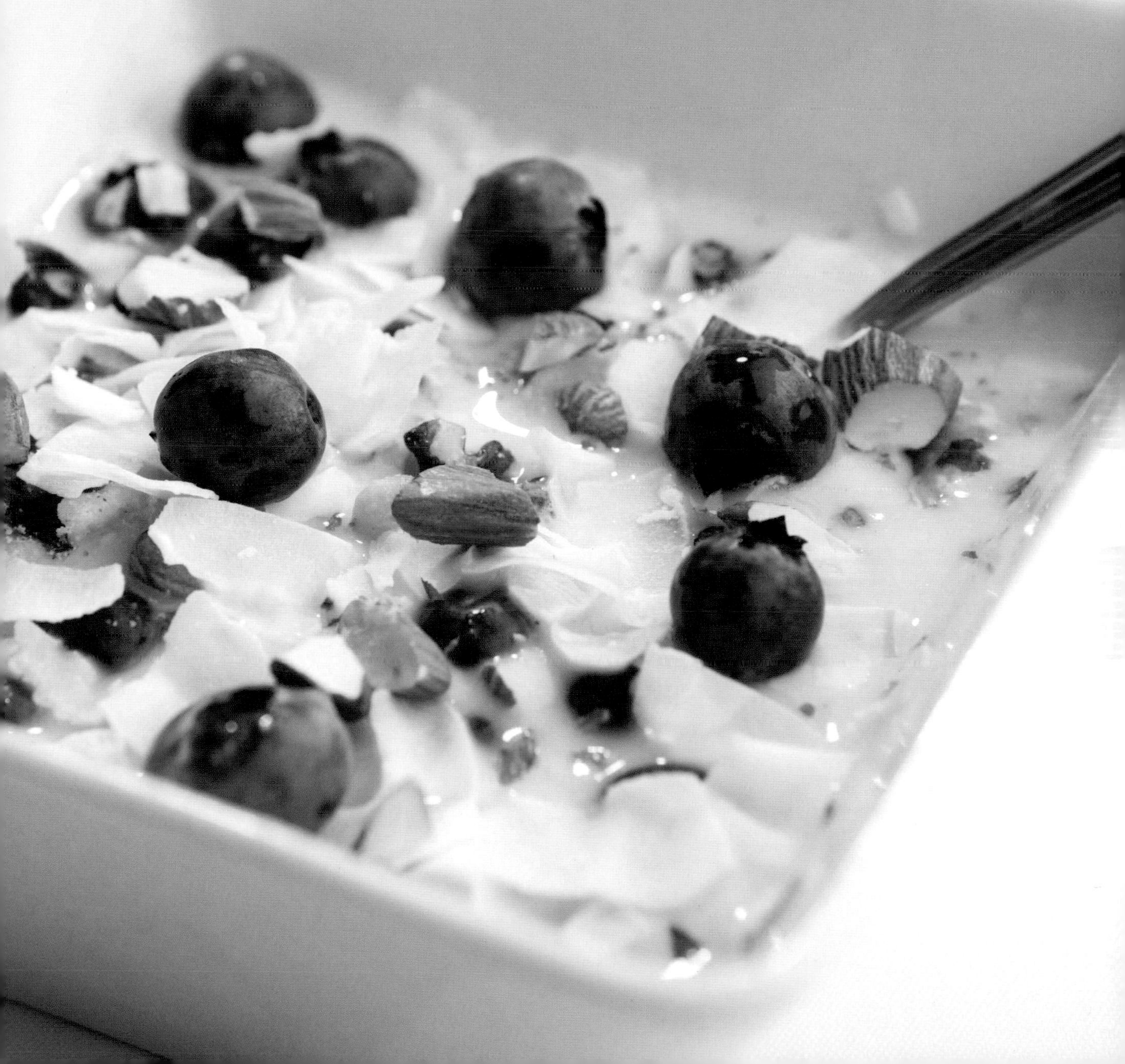

CREAMY BERRY PARFAIT

SERVES 2-4

NUT MIX

½ cup raw almonds
½ cup raw walnuts
¼ cup raw pumpkin seeds
¼ cup raw sunflower seeds
¼ cup raw flaxseeds

RAW CASHEW VANILLA CREAM

1 cup raw cashews, soaked
   and drained
¼ to ½ cup filtered water
1 tablespoon raw coconut
   nectar (I like Coconut Secret®)
½ teaspoon pure vanilla extract
Pinch sea salt

BERRIES

1 cup fresh blueberries
1 cup fresh raspberries

Chef V's Tips: Many raw-food recipes call for soaking nuts. Why? Soaking nuts (from 2 hours to overnight) improves the flavor and nutritional value of the nuts by releasing dust, residue, and tannins into the water, leaving the nuts with a softer, buttery texture and increasing their digestibility. Never use the soak water; always discard it. And, for easy breakfast planning, my Raw Cashew Vanilla Cream recipe can easily be doubled and will keep for up to a week refrigerated.

Combine all the nut mix ingredients in a bowl. Next, process the Raw Cashew Vanilla Cream ingredients in a Vitamix until smooth and creamy.

To serve, assemble the parfait in a mason jar or clear glass:
Step 1: Place ½ of the nuts on the bottom.
Step 2: Sprinkle ½ of the berries over the nuts.
Step 3: Spoon the cashew cream over the top.
Step 4: Sprinkle the remaining nuts over the cream.
Step 5: Garnish with remaining berries.

V R P DF GF KF

CHEF V'S FOOD FACT:
FLAXSEEDS ARE A RICH SOURCE OF MICRONUTRIENTS, DIETARY FIBER, MANGANESE, VITAMIN B1, AND THE ESSENTIAL OMEGA-3 FATTY ACID.

WARM CINNAMON QUINOA
SERVES 4

QUINOA

**1 cup uncooked quinoa,
   rinsed and drained**
**1 cup Chef V's Raw Almond
   Milk** *(See recipe, page 32)*
   or coconut milk
1 cup filtered water
**1 tablespoon raw coconut
   nectar (I like Coconut
   Secret®)**
½ teaspoon ground cinnamon

OPTIONAL TOPPINGS

2 cups fresh blackberries
⅓ cup raw pecans, chopped

Chef V's Tip: My fail-proof way to cook quinoa is to use a rice cooker. Place 1 cup uncooked quinoa and 2 cups liquid (either 2 cups filtered water or 1 cup filtered water and 1 cup unsweetened almond milk or coconut milk) in the cooker and set it on the white rice setting. The quinoa comes out perfect every time. If you don't have a rice cooker, place the quinoa and 2 cups liquid in a medium-sized pot. Bring to a boil, reduce the heat to medium, and cover with a tight-fitting lid. Simmer, covered, for about 15-20 minutes, or until all of the water is absorbed. Remove the pan from the heat, fluff the quinoa with a fork, and keep it covered until ready to use.

Cook the quinoa in a rice cooker, or, if cooking on a stovetop, follow the directions in Chef V's Tip above except simmer for 15 minutes, or until most of the liquid is absorbed. Turn off the heat and let the quinoa stand, covered, for 5 minutes. Stir in the coconut nectar and cinnamon. To serve, spoon into bowls and top with blackberries and pecans.

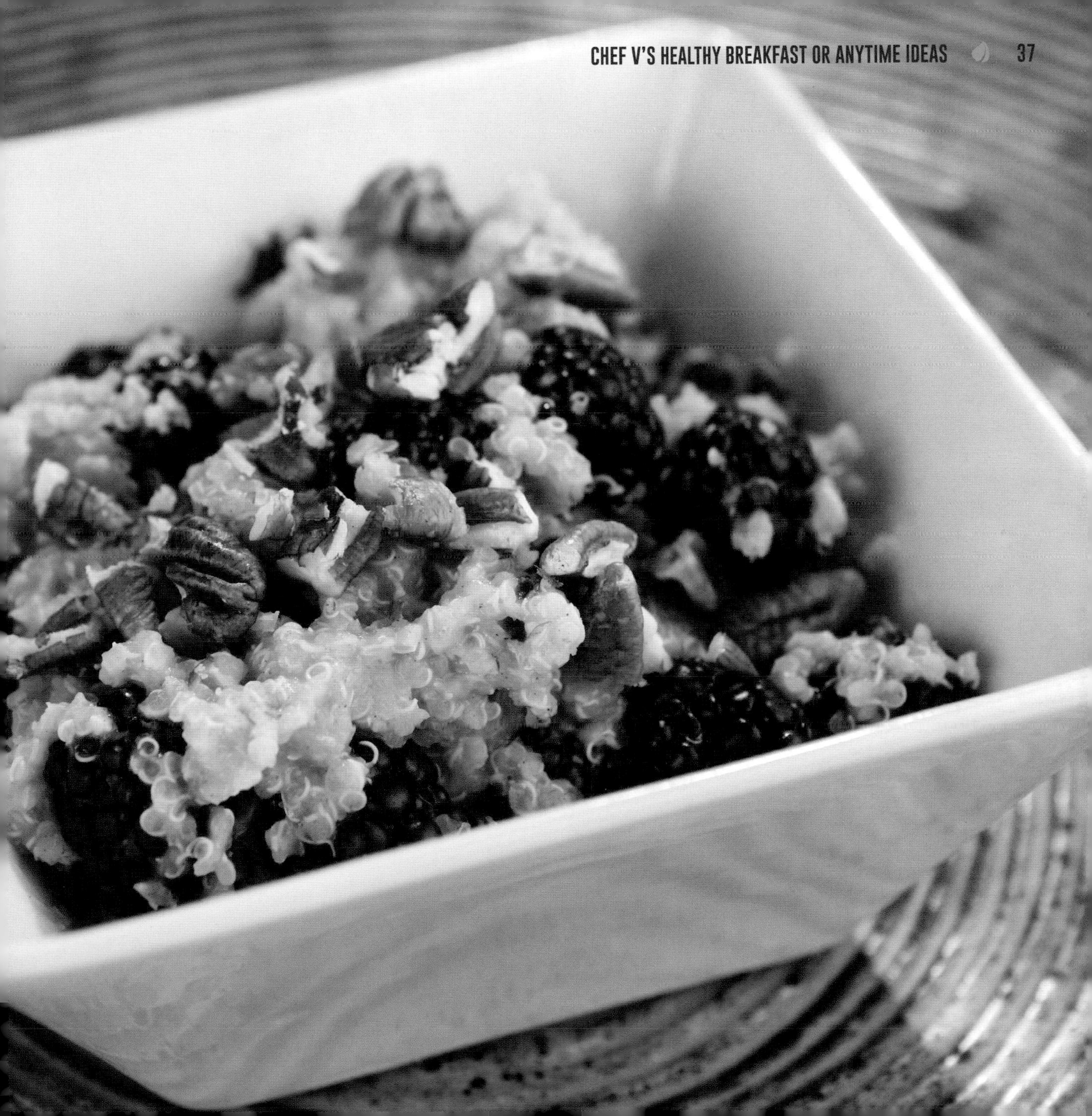

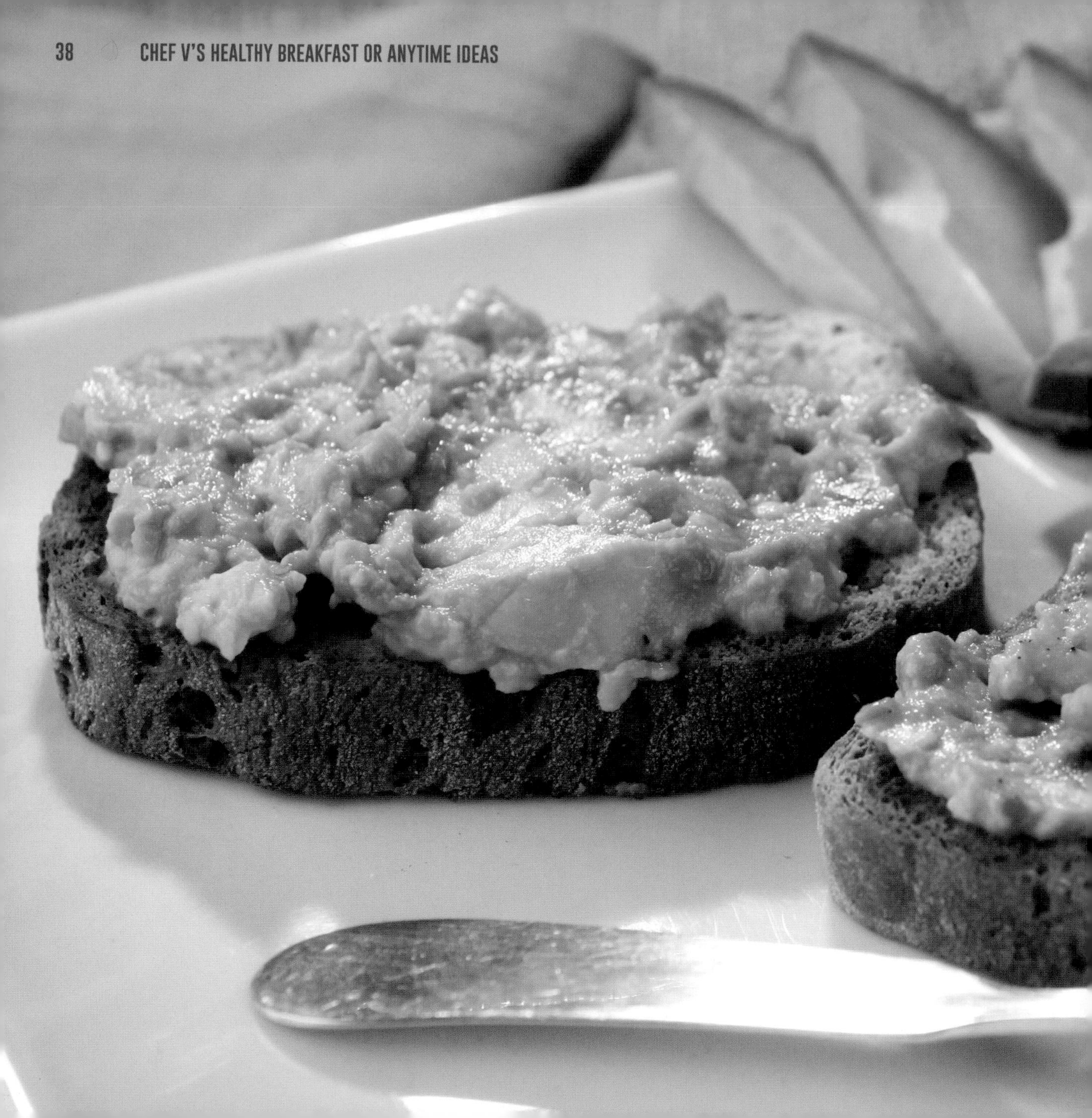

GLUTEN-FREE TOAST + AVOCADO SMEAR
SERVES 1

1 slice gluten-free bread or
  ½ gluten-free bagel
¼ ripe avocado, smashed

OPTIONAL TOPPINGS
Fresh lemon juice
Apple cider vinegar
**Pinch cayenne pepper or
  red pepper flakes**
Pinch sea salt

Lightly toast the bread and
spread the avocado on like
butter. For extra pizzazz,
add a dash of lemon juice,
apple cider vinegar, cayenne
pepper, or sea salt, if desired.

*Chef V's Tip: Add a
dash of lemon, sea salt,
and red pepper flakes
for extra flavor.*

V DF GF KF

BREAKFAST CARPACCIO

SERVES 1

4 ounces smoked wild salmon, sliced thin
1 tablespoon lemon juice
½ ripe avocado, sliced thin
Sliced red onion
1 teaspoon capers
1 slice gluten-free bread
**   or bagel, optional**

Soak the salmon in the lemon juice for a minute. Plate the salmon and top it with avocado, onions, and capers. Or you can eat the salmon on gluten-free toast or bagel. **P** **DF** **GF**

Be creative! Top your gluten-free toast + avocado smear with smoked salmon and other toppings.

CHEF V'S FOOD FACT:
AVOCADOS ARE A NUTRITIONIST'S
DREAM FOOD — PACKED WITH NEARLY
20 ESSENTIAL NUTRIENTS, INCLUDING
FIBER, POTASSIUM, VITAMIN E, B
VITAMINS, AND FOLIC ACID.

what the symbols mean:
vegan • raw • paleo • dairy-free
gluten-free • kid friendly
V R P DF GF KF

CHEF V'S
TASTY SNACKS + APPS

Let me let you in on a little secret — snacking isn't a bad thing if you pick the right nutritionally dense foods and, of course, eat in moderation. Healthy snacks can boost energy levels and satisfy those hunger pains you get *between* meals. Nibble, not gobble. Here are some of my go-to snacks to help you crush your cravings and avoid sabotaging your new healthy lifestyle. These also double as easy appetizers for entertaining. Always have on hand: fresh blueberries, raspberries, blackberries, celery, carrots (not pre-bagged or frozen), cucumbers, avocados, pears, apples, pomegranate seeds, raw unsalted nuts (my favs are almonds and walnuts), and even a few dried berries.

CHEF V'S FOOD FACT:
FIGS HAVE A WONDERFULLY SWEET TASTE AND A SOFT AND
CHEWY TEXTURE. THEY ARE FULL OF POTASSIUM, CALCIUM, IRON,
COPPER, MAGNESIUM, AND ANTIOXIDANT VITAMINS A, E, AND K.

ALMOND NUT CHEESE
SERVES 4

Chef V's Tip: Great for parties, tossed in salads, or spread on sandwiches.

1 cup raw almonds, soaked and drained with skins removed
(See tip, page 35)
3 tablespoons fresh lemon juice
2 tablespoons cold-pressed olive oil
¾ cup filtered water

1 clove garlic
¼ teaspoon sea salt

OPTIONAL GARNISHES

Fresh berries, figs, gluten-free crackers, and mixed greens

Process all ingredients in a Vitamix until smooth. This will take some time. Place the mixture in a nut-milk bag or colander lined with cheesecloth, give it a light squeeze, and place in the refrigerator overnight. Remove the cheese from the cloth. Cheese is now ready to serve, or for firmer cheese, place it in a dehydrator for 6+ hours at 115°F to form a rind. Cheese will keep refrigerated for up to 1 week. Serve with your favorite fresh berries, figs, greens or gluten-free crackers.

V R P DF GF KF

EASY TRAIL MIX
SERVES 4

Chef V's Tip: Try different ingredients to create some fun mixes. I generally use one or two raw nuts, one seed, and one dried fruit. Some ideas for nuts: almonds, walnuts, pistachios, cashews, pecans, or macadamia nuts. For dried fruit, always choose unsweetened and unsulfured fruits. My favorites include Goji berries, pineapple, apple, mango, and blueberries.

1 cup raw almonds
1 cup raw walnuts
¼ cup unsweetened dried Goji berries
¼ cup raw sunflower seeds, sprouted if available

Combine all the ingredients in a resealable bag or a bowl. I keep a bag in my car and a bowl handy in the house for easy and healthy munching wherever I am.

CHEF V'S FOOD FACT:
THE GOJI IS A TART-TASTING BRIGHT RED BERRY NATIVE TO ASIA THAT IS A POPULAR NATURAL FOOD. ITS LEVEL OF VITAMIN C IS COMPARABLE TO MANY CITRUS FRUITS, PLUS IT HAS BETA-CAROTENE AND ANTIOXIDANTS.

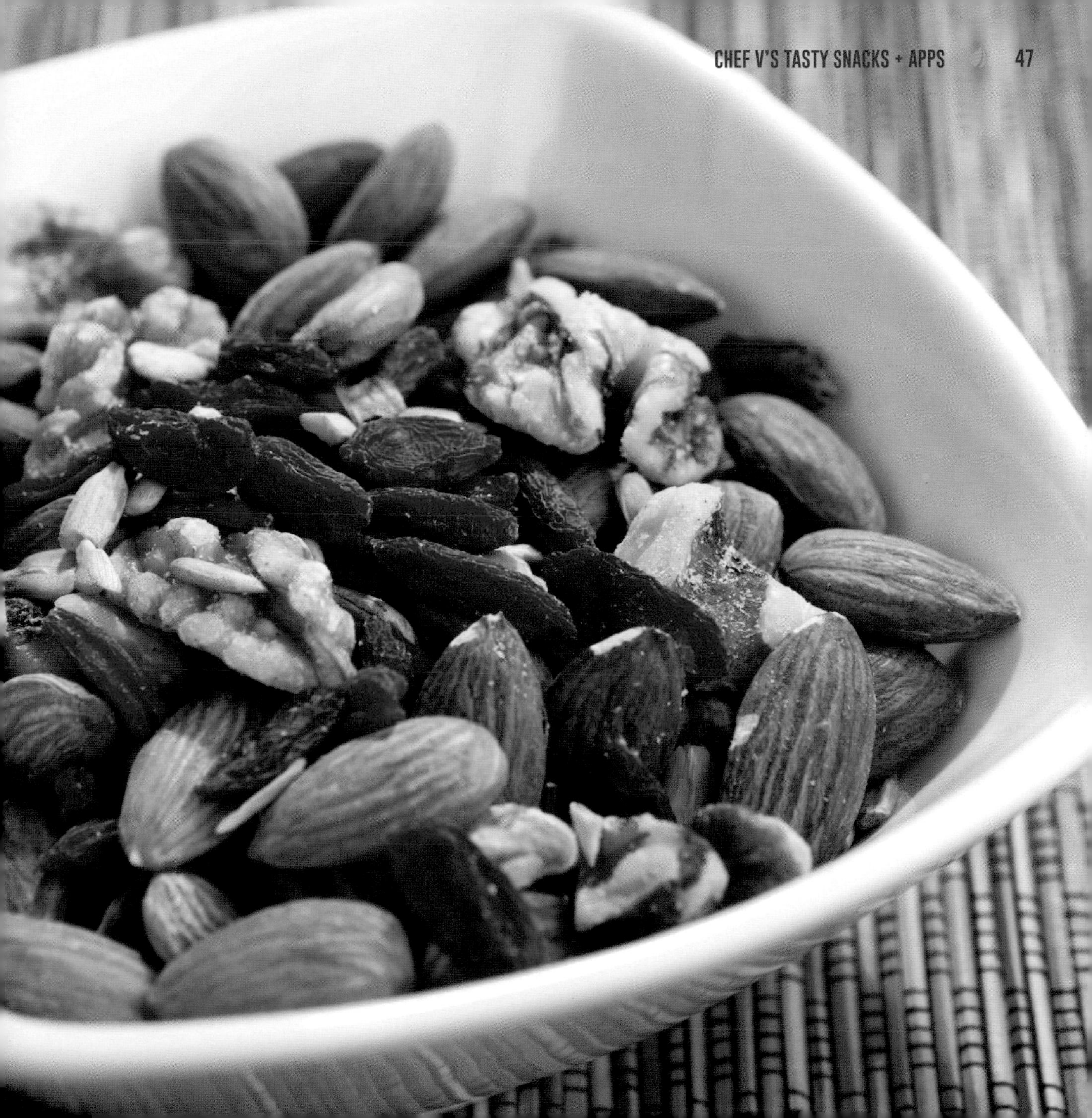

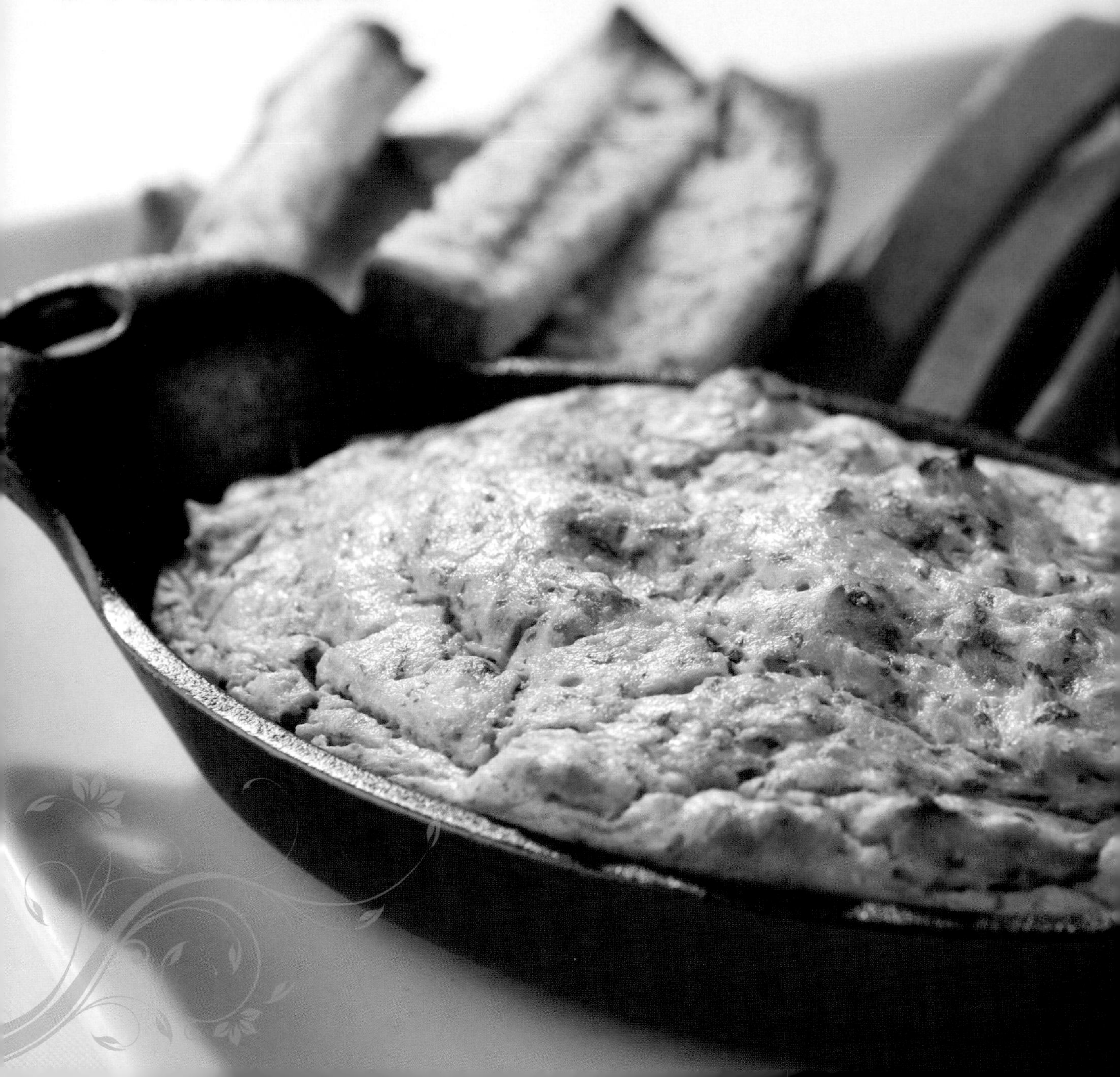

SPINACH ARTICHOKE DIP
SERVES 4-6

Chef V's Tip: I love using garlic in my cooking, but it's kind of a hassle to mince because it is so small. My trick for you — use a presser. It is one of my favorite tools in my kitchen. Just peel the garlic, pop it into the presser, and presto!

¾ cup raw cashews, unsoaked
¾ cup **Chef V's Raw Almond Milk** *(See recipe, page 32)*
 or coconut milk
2 to 3 tablespoons fresh lemon juice
2 cloves garlic, minced or pressed
1 teaspoon sea salt
½ teaspoon dry mustard
1½ cups canned artichoke hearts (or partially thaw
 if using frozen)
2 cups fresh spinach

OPTIONAL SIDES
Fresh veggies, gluten-free crackers and bread

Preheat the oven to 425°F. Process all the ingredients except artichoke and spinach in a Vitamix until smooth. Add the artichoke and spinach. Pulse but do not blend. Transfer the mixture to a 6x6-inch dish, or to multiple small oven-safe dishes, and bake for 20 minutes. Remove the dip and let cool for 5 minutes before serving. Enjoy with gluten-free bread, crackers, or your favorite veggies. Ⓥ Ⓟ ⒹⒻ ⒼⒻ ⓀⒻ

EASY HUMMUS

SERVES 2-4

1 (15-ounce) can or 2 cups cooked garbanzo beans, chilled
1 lemon, juiced
1 tablespoon tahini paste
1 tablespoon cold-pressed olive oil
1 clove garlic, minced or pressed
1 teaspoon sea salt
¼ teaspoon ground cumin
1 cucumber, seeded and sliced

OPTIONAL TOPPINGS

¼ teaspoon smoked paprika
White or black sesame seeds

Process all ingredients except cucumber in a Vitamix for 1 to 2 minutes. Add 1 tablespoon of water if needed for better blending. Serve on cucumber slices, as a dip with your favorite veggies, or spread on a wrap or gluten-free toast. Sprinkle with paprika and sesame seeds.

CHEF V'S RAW ALMOND BUTTER

SERVES 1

3 cups raw almonds

Process the nuts in Vitamix for 10-20 minutes. This is easy, but it takes patience. After about 5 minutes, the nuts will look like almond flour. After another 5-10 minutes, the oils will start seeping out of the mixture, forming a paste, and then finally the butter emerges! Store in a sealed mason jar. Will keep refrigerated for up to a month.

SNACK IDEAS
1 large celery stick
1 tablespoon Chef V's Raw Almond Butter

OPTIONAL TOPPINGS
1 tablespoon unsweetened shredded coconut
¼ teaspoon ground cinnamon
1 teaspoon raw cacao nibs

Remove the outer skin of the celery and cut the stalk in half or thirds. Smear my almond butter on, sprinkle with your favorite toppings, and start crunching!

APPLES WITH CHEF V'S RAW ALMOND BUTTER + COCONUT

SERVES 1-2

1 apple (my favs are Fuji, Honeycrisp, and Gala)
2 tablespoons Chef V's Raw Almond Butter *(See recipe, page 53)*

OPTIONAL TOPPINGS
1 tablespoon unsweetened
   shredded coconut
¼ teaspoon ground cinnamon
1 teaspoon raw cacao nibs

Cut the apple in quarters
and smear the almond
butter on. Sprinkle with
toppings if desired,
and savor each bite!

(V) (R) (P) (DF) (GF) (KF)

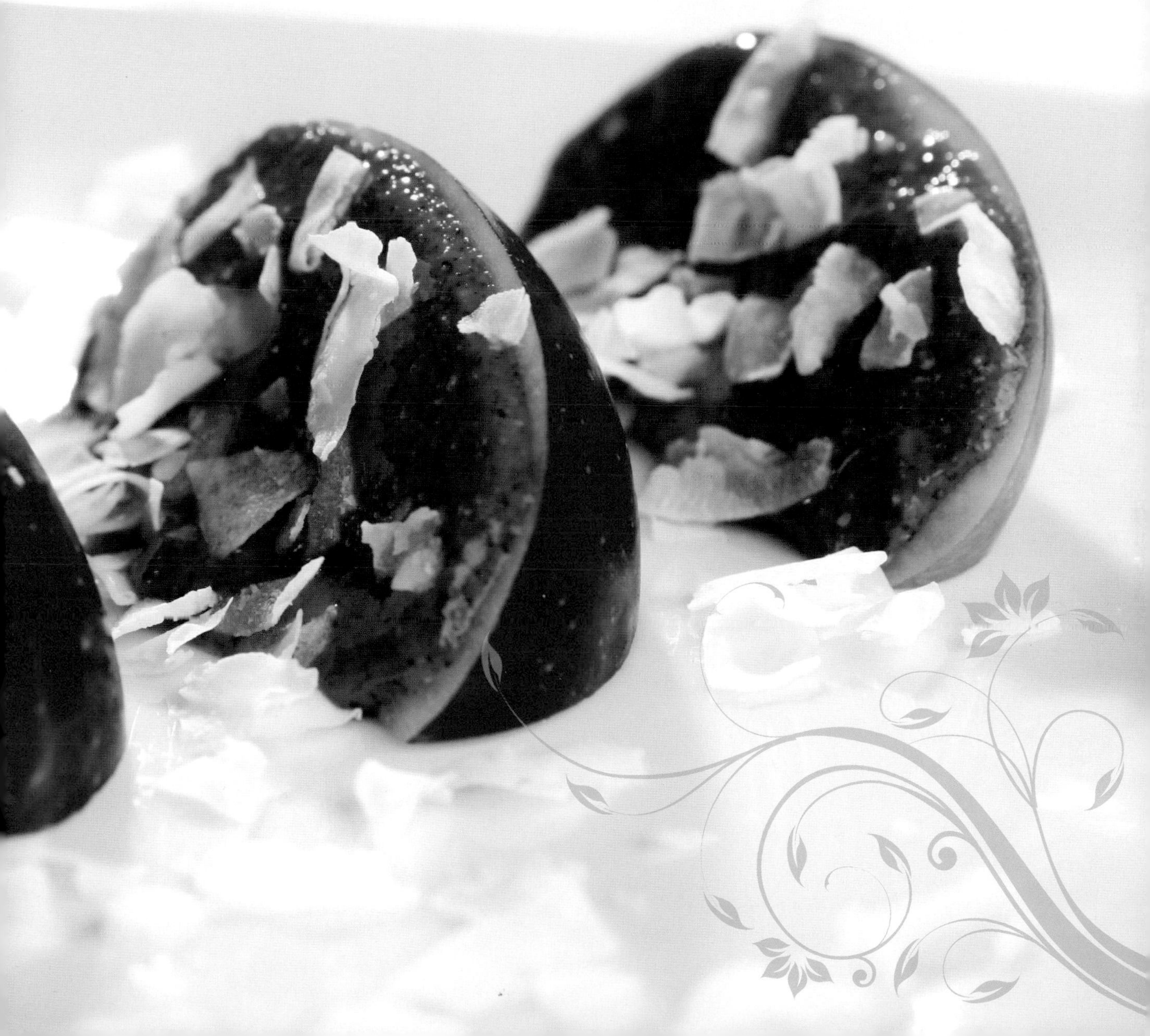

CHEF V'S FRUIT JAM + RAW ALMOND BUTTER SANDWICH

SERVES 1

FRUIT JAM

4 cups fresh raspberries
2 whole apples, peeled, cored, and diced
1½ cups fresh apple juice

SANDWICH

2 slices gluten-free bread
½ tablespoon Chef V's Fruit Jam
½ tablespoon Chef V's Raw Almond Butter
(See recipe, page 53)

To make the fruit jam, bring all the jam ingredients to boil in a medium saucepan. Reduce the heat and simmer for 45 minutes. Remove from the heat and let cool. Place in an airtight jar or container. Will keep for 2-4 weeks refrigerated.

Toast the bread, if desired. Spread the fruit jam on one half, the almond butter on the other, and enjoy!

EASY APPLE SAUCE
SERVES 2

5 apples, peeled, cored, and cut into pieces
   (my favs are Fuji, Honeycrisp, and Gala)
1 cup filtered water, or more as needed
⅛ teaspoon cinnamon

Boil the apples in the water for 10 minutes.
Drain the water and transfer the apple pieces
to a Vitamix, add cinnamon, and process for
2 minutes for smooth consistency or 1 minute
for chunky. V P DF GF KF

what the symbols mean:
vegan · raw · paleo · dairy-free
gluten-free · kid friendly

V R P DF GF KF

CHEF V'S
SUPER SOUPS

Warm and creamy, cool and comforting, soups are a great way to start a meal, but are also awesome as a meal. You can easily double or triple my recipes and have delicious leftovers on hand for easy meal-planning. The beauty of my veggie-rich recipes is that their high water and fiber content slows how fast you eat and fills you up quicker. I have packed my soups with lots of flavorful herbs and spices and some gluten-free grains, like quinoa, which add a nice texture and nutritional boost, too. Always try to use the freshest organically grown food.

MEDITERRANEAN BUTTERNUT SQUASH + CARROT STEW WITH QUINOA

SERVES 4

Chef V's Tip: This stew can be prepared a day ahead. It's great to take to work or enjoy for dinner the next day or for a warm and healthy meal for the kids to come home to and easily reheat.

STEW

2 tablespoons cold-pressed
   olive oil

1 cup white onion, diced

3 cloves garlic, minced or pressed

2 teaspoons sweet paprika

1 teaspoon sea salt

½ teaspoon each: black pepper,
   ground coriander, ground
   cumin, ground turmeric,
   ground ginger, and cayenne
   pepper

Pinch saffron

1 cup filtered water

1 cup cooked lentils
   (if canned, do not drain;
   if cooked, save ¼ cup
   of the cooking water)

2 tablespoons fresh lemon juice

3 cups (about 1½ pounds) cubed
   butternut squash

2 cups peeled carrots, cut into
   ¾-inch slices   ≫

First prepare the stew. Heat the oil in a large saucepan over medium heat. Add the onion and sauté until soft, stirring often, about 5 minutes. Add the garlic and stir for 1 minute. Add the dry spices. Add 1 cup of water, lentils (with liquid from the can or reserved ¼ cup cooking water), and lemon juice. Bring the mixture to a boil. Add the squash and carrots. Cover and simmer over medium-low heat. Stir occasionally and cook for about 20 minutes, or until the vegetables are tender. Keep warm until the quinoa is finished, or cover the stew and refrigerate until ready to serve.

Next prepare the quinoa. Place the oil in a large saucepan over medium heat. Add the onion and cook, covered, until translucent, about 3 to 5 minutes, stirring often so the onion does not burn. Add the garlic, salt, and turmeric, and sauté for 1 minute. Add the quinoa and stir for 1 minute. Add 2 cups of water. Bring to a boil and then reduce the heat to medium-low. Cover and simmer until all the liquid is absorbed and the quinoa is tender, about 15 minutes.

To serve, stir half of the cilantro and half of the basil into the warm stew. Spoon the quinoa onto a platter or divide among bowls and form a well in the center. Spoon the stew into the well and garnish with the remaining cilantro and basil, if desired.

(V) (DF) (GF) (KF)

QUINOA

1 tablespoon cold-pressed
  olive oil
½ cup diced white onion
2 garlic cloves, minced
⅓ teaspoon sea salt
½ teaspoon ground turmeric
1 cup uncooked quinoa,
  rinsed and drained
2 cups filtered water

OPTIONAL TOPPINGS

½ cup chopped fresh
  cilantro
¼ cup chopped fresh
  basil

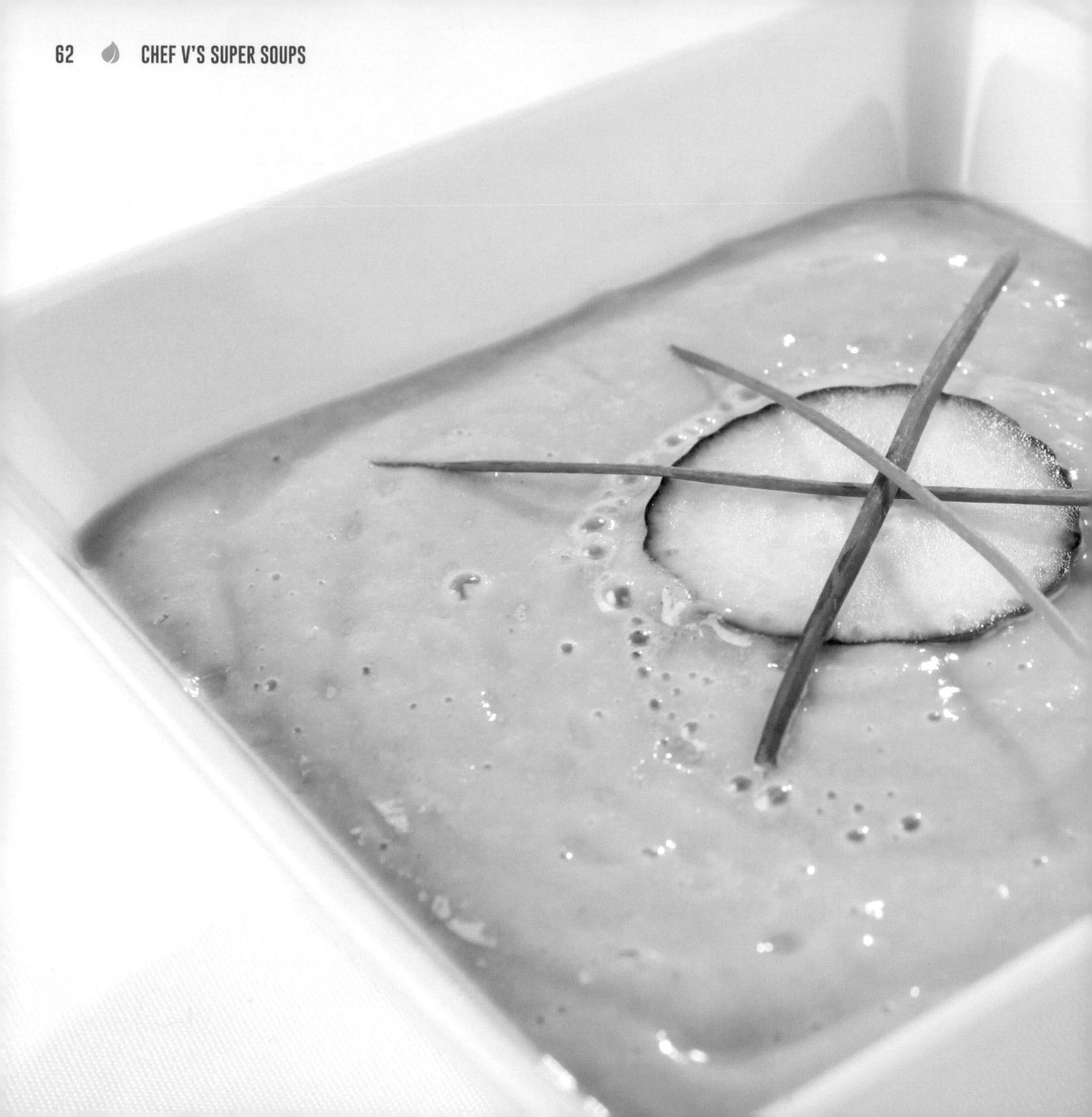

RAW CUCUMBER + AVOCADO GAZPACHO

SERVES 2-4

1 ripe avocado
1 cucumber
½ cup fresh cilantro leaves
1 clove garlic
2 tablespoons chopped fresh chives
2 cups filtered ice water
1¼ teaspoons sea salt
1 lime, juice only

OPTIONAL TOPPINGS
Fresh chopped chives
Cucumber slices

Refrigerate all the ingredients overnight. Peel and seed the avocado and peel the cucumber and garlic. Place all the cold ingredients in a Vitamix and process until smooth. The colder the ingredients are, the less foam there will be. Serve cold and top with chives and cucumber slices.

(V) (R) (P) (DF) (GF)

SPICY VEGGIE SOUP

SERVES 4-6

½ tablespoon coconut oil
3 cloves garlic, minced or pressed
2 cups sweet onion, diced
1 jalapeño, seeded (if preferred) and chopped
1 to 2 (2½ to 3 cups) large zucchini, diced
   into ½-inch pieces
1½ teaspoons ground cumin
1 teaspoon chili powder
½ teaspoon ground coriander
6 cups vegetable broth
1 cup cooked quinoa *(See tip, page 36)*
1½ cups cooked or 1 (15-ounce) can black beans,
   drained and rinsed
¼ teaspoon cayenne pepper or red pepper flakes
1 cup spinach or kale leaves
Sea salt and freshly ground black pepper

OPTIONAL TOPPINGS
Avocado, cilantro, and green onion

Heat the oil in a stockpot over medium heat. Add the garlic and onion, and sauté for a few minutes. Add the jalapeño and zucchini, and sauté for 5 to 7 minutes more. Stir in the cumin, chili powder, coriander, and broth. Bring to a boil. Reduce heat to medium and simmer for about 15 minutes, uncovered. Just before serving, stir in the cooked quinoa, black beans, cayenne, and greens. Season with salt and pepper to taste. Garnish with avocado, cilantro, and green onion.

Ⓥ ⒹⒻ ⒼⒻ

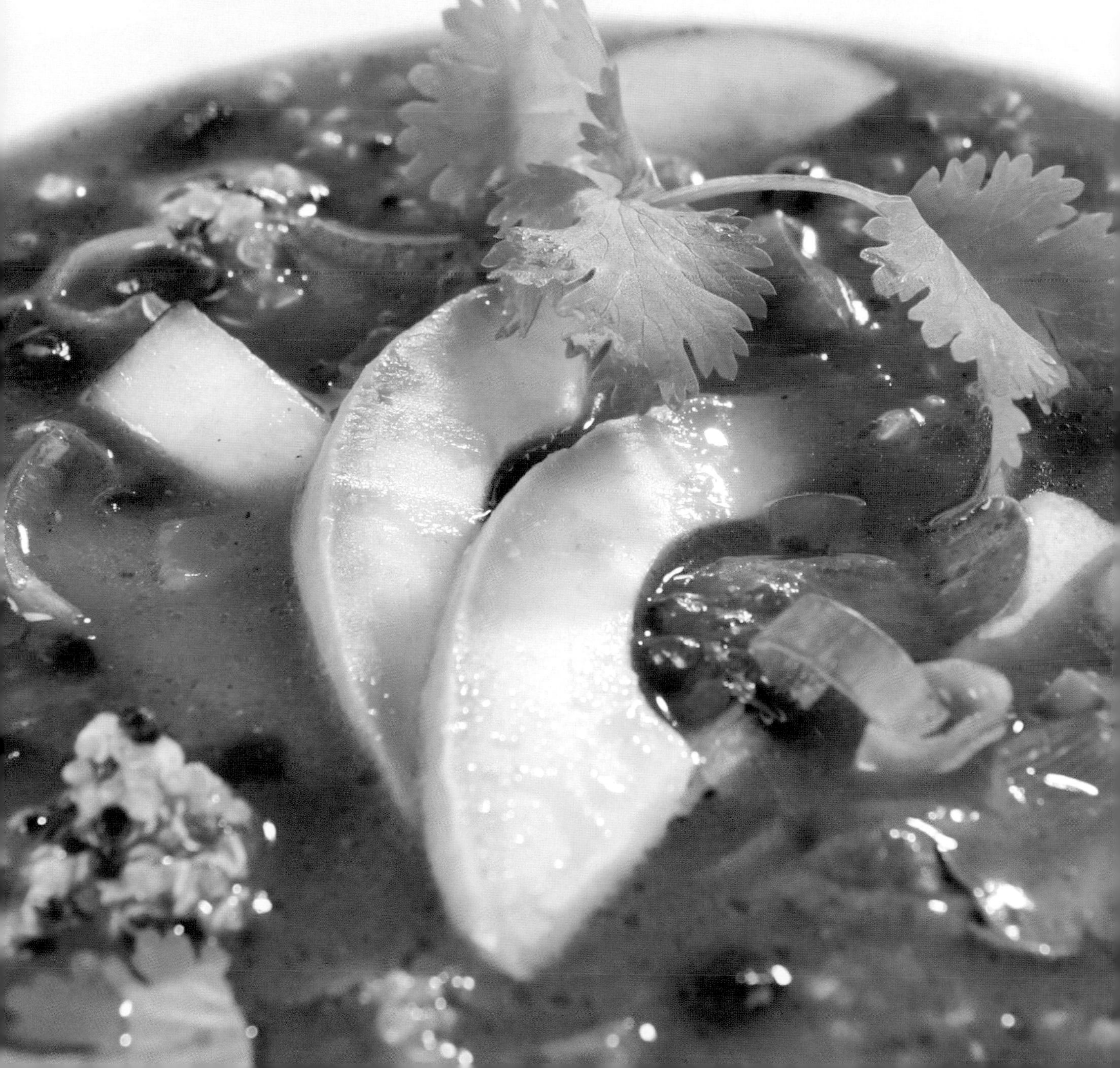

CREAMY BEET SOUP

SERVES 4

- 1 tablespoon cold-pressed olive oil
- 1 cup onion, diced
- 3 cloves garlic, minced or pressed
- 3 cups vegetable broth
- 3 large beets, peeled and chopped
- 1 medium sweet potato, peeled and cubed
- 1 cup unsweetened coconut milk
- 1 bay leaf
- 1 teaspoon sea salt
- 1 teaspoon red pepper flakes, optional

Heat the oil in a large stockpot. Add onion and sauté for 2 minutes. Add garlic and continue to cook for 1 minute, or until onion is translucent. Add broth, beets, sweet potato, coconut milk, and bay leaf. Boil for 20 minutes, or until beet and sweet potato become tender. Remove the bay leaf. Transfer to a Vitamix and process in batches until smooth. Add salt and red pepper to taste.

V **P** **DF** **GF**

CHEF V'S FOOD FACT: BEETS, INCLUDING BEET GREENS, CONTAIN AN AMAZING ARRAY OF ANTIOXIDANTS, OTHER VITAMINS, MINERALS, FIBER, AND PROTEIN. THEY ARE ALSO BELIEVED TO SUPPORT OUR BODY'S DETOX SYSTEM AS WELL AS HAVING ANTI-CANCER AND ANTI-INFLAMMATORY PROPERTIES.

GREEN SOUP WITH LEMON BASIL PESTO

SERVES 4

1 to 2 tablespoons cold-pressed olive oil
1 cup celery, thinly sliced
1 cup leeks, thinly sliced
2 teaspoons garlic, minced or pressed
¼ teaspoon sea salt
3 cups vegetable stock
1 cup filtered water
7 thyme sprigs, divided use
1 cup fresh or frozen peas
1 cup fresh green beans, cut into 1-inch pieces

1 (15-ounce) can cannellini beans, drained
1 cup baby spinach leaves

BASIL PESTO

1 cup baby spinach leaves
1 cup fresh basil
2 teaspoons lemon zest
1 tablespoon fresh lemon juice
1 teaspoon garlic, minced or pressed
2 teaspoons cold-pressed olive oil

Heat the olive oil in a large stockpot or Dutch oven over medium heat. Add the celery, leeks, garlic, and sea salt. Sauté for 5 minutes. Add the stock, water, and 3 thyme sprigs. Cover and bring the mixture to a boil. Add the peas, green beans, and cannellini beans. Simmer, uncovered, for 5 minutes. Discard the thyme sprigs. Stir in the spinach.

Make the basil pesto sauce. Process all of the pesto ingredients in a Vitamix until smooth.

Ladle the soup into 4 bowls. Top each with the pesto and thyme sprigs and serve. Ⓥ Ⓟ ⒹⒻ ⒼⒻ ⓀⒻ

CREAMY BROCCOLI SOUP

SERVES 2

1 large yellow onion, diced

3 shallots, minced or pressed

2 cloves garlic, minced or
   pressed

2 tablespoons coconut oil

4 cups vegetable broth

6 cups chopped broccoli
   florets

1 tablespoon fresh thyme
   leaves

½ cup coconut milk

½ cup raw cashews,
   soaked and drained
   (See tip, page 35)

½ cup raw pumpkin seeds

Chef V's Tip: In case you didn't know, coconut milk is the liquid that comes from the grated meat of a brown coconut, whereas coconut water is the clear liquid inside young green coconuts. When using canned coconut milk, shake the can first to even out the creamy thickness of the milk inside. Once opened, cans of coconut milk must be refrigerated and are usually only good for a few days.

In a large stockpot over medium-high heat, sauté the onions, shallots, and garlic in the coconut oil and cook for about 3 to 4 minutes, or until the onions are translucent. Add the broth and broccoli and boil for 10 minutes, or until the broccoli is just tender. Transfer to a Vitamix in batches, if necessary, and process until smooth. Add thyme, coconut milk, and cashews and blend again until smooth. Top with raw pumpkin seeds and serve.

(V) (P) (DF) (GF) (KF)

CHEF V'S FOOD FACT:
COCONUT OIL IS EXCELLENT
TO COOK WITH. IT INCREASES
DIGESTION, HELPS ABSORB FAT-
SOLUBLE VITAMINS, AND HAS
BEEN SHOWN TO POSITIVELY
AFFECT OUR HORMONES AND
BLOOD SUGAR LEVELS.

TOMATO-LESS CHILI
SERVES 4-6

Chef V's Tips: While I generally do not use a lot of nightshade vegetables, I do think fresh or dried jalapeño peppers in small quantities add a kick to dishes and have detoxifying powers. For more protein, swap the cannellini beans with 1 pound of cooked ground turkey, if desired.

1 tablespoon cold-pressed olive oil
1 medium yellow onion, diced
3 cloves garlic, minced or pressed
5 tablespoons chili powder
2 teaspoons ground cumin
2 teaspoons dried oregano
4 cups vegetable broth
1 (15-ounce) can of each: kidney, cannellini,
   and black beans, drained and rinsed
2 tablespoons chili sauce,
   or to taste (I like Trader Joe's® brand)

OPTIONAL TOPPINGS
Sliced and seeded jalapeño pepper
¼ cup Daiya® cheddar shreds

Heat oil in a large soup pot over medium heat. Add the onion and garlic, and sauté for about 3 minutes. Stir in chili powder, cumin, and oregano and cook for another 2 minutes. Reduce the heat to low, and add the vegetable broth, kidney beans, cannellini, black beans, and chili sauce. Cover and simmer for about 35 minutes. To serve, ladle into bowls and garnish with sliced jalapeños or cheddar shreds, if desired. Ⓥ Ⓟ ⒹⒻ ⒼⒻ ⓀⒻ

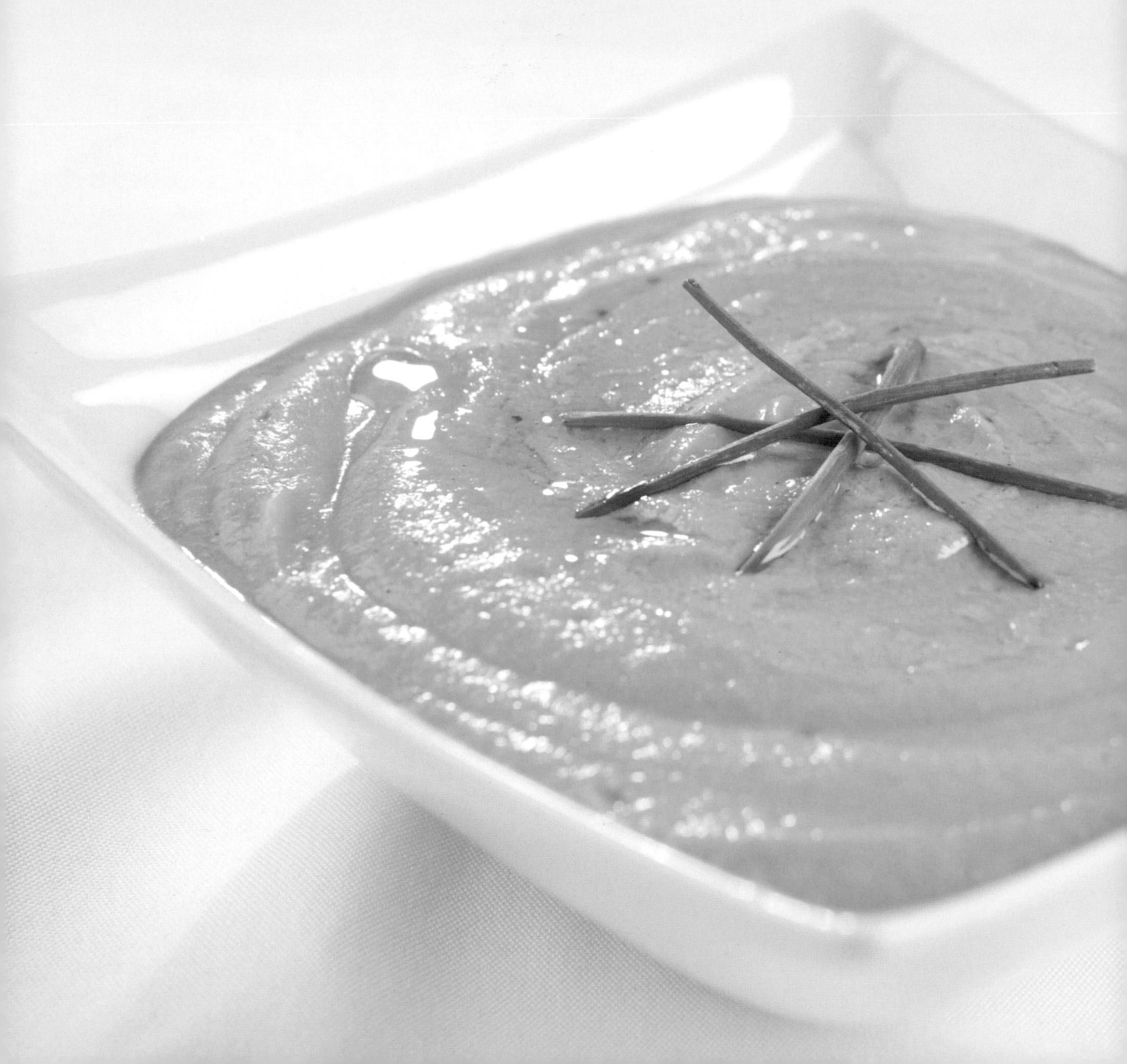

CREAMY CARROT SOUP
SERVES 2

1 to 2 teaspoons coconut oil or cold-pressed olive oil
3 cloves garlic, minced or pressed
2 cups sweet onion, diced
1½ pounds (about 5 cups) carrots, peeled and chopped
5 cups vegetable broth
2 to 3 tablespoons grated fresh ginger
¾ cup raw cashews, soaked and drained *(See tip, page 35)*
½ cup Chef V's Raw Almond Milk *(See recipe, page 32)*
   or coconut milk
Sea salt and freshly ground black pepper, to taste

OPTIONAL TOPPINGS
Fresh chives, flat-leaf parsley, raw cashews, optional

Heat the oil in a large stockpot over medium heat. Add the garlic and onion and sauté for 3 to 5 minutes, or until the onion is translucent. Add the carrots, vegetable broth, and 2 to 3 tablespoons of grated ginger. Bring to a boil. Reduce the heat and simmer for about 20 minutes, or until the carrots are tender. Turn off the heat and allow the soup to cool for 10 minutes. Drain and rinse the cashews well. Add the cashews and almond milk or coconut milk to the soup. Transfer to a Vitamix in batches, if necessary, and process until smooth. Taste the soup and season with salt and pepper, if desired. To serve, ladle the soup into bowls and garnish as desired. Ⓥ Ⓟ Ⓓ🇫 Ⓖ🇫 Ⓚ🇫

CREAMY SWEET POTATO + LEEK SOUP
SERVES 4

1 to 2 leeks, chopped
1 clove garlic, minced or pressed
1 tablespoon coconut oil
1 pound sweet potatoes, peeled and chopped
½ pound white carrots, peeled and chopped
4 cups vegetable broth
½ cup raw cashews, soaked and drained *(See tip, page 35)*

In a saucepan, sauté the leek and garlic in the coconut oil for 2 minutes over medium heat. Add the sweet potatoes, carrots, and vegetable broth and bring to a boil. Reduce heat to low and cook for 15 to 20 minutes, until the veggies are tender. Add the cashews. Transfer to a Vitamix in batches, if necessary, and process until smooth. Soup is best served warm. (V) (P) (DF) (GF) (KF)

CHEF V'S FOOD FACT:
SWEET POTATOES ARE THE UBER TUBER — PACKED WITH FIBER AND ANTIOXIDANT, ANTI-INFLAMMATORY, AND BLOOD SUGAR-REGULATING NUTRIENTS. THE BEST WAYS TO PREPARE THEM FOR MAXIMUM HEALTH BENEFITS ARE BOILING, STEAMING, AND STIR-FRYING.

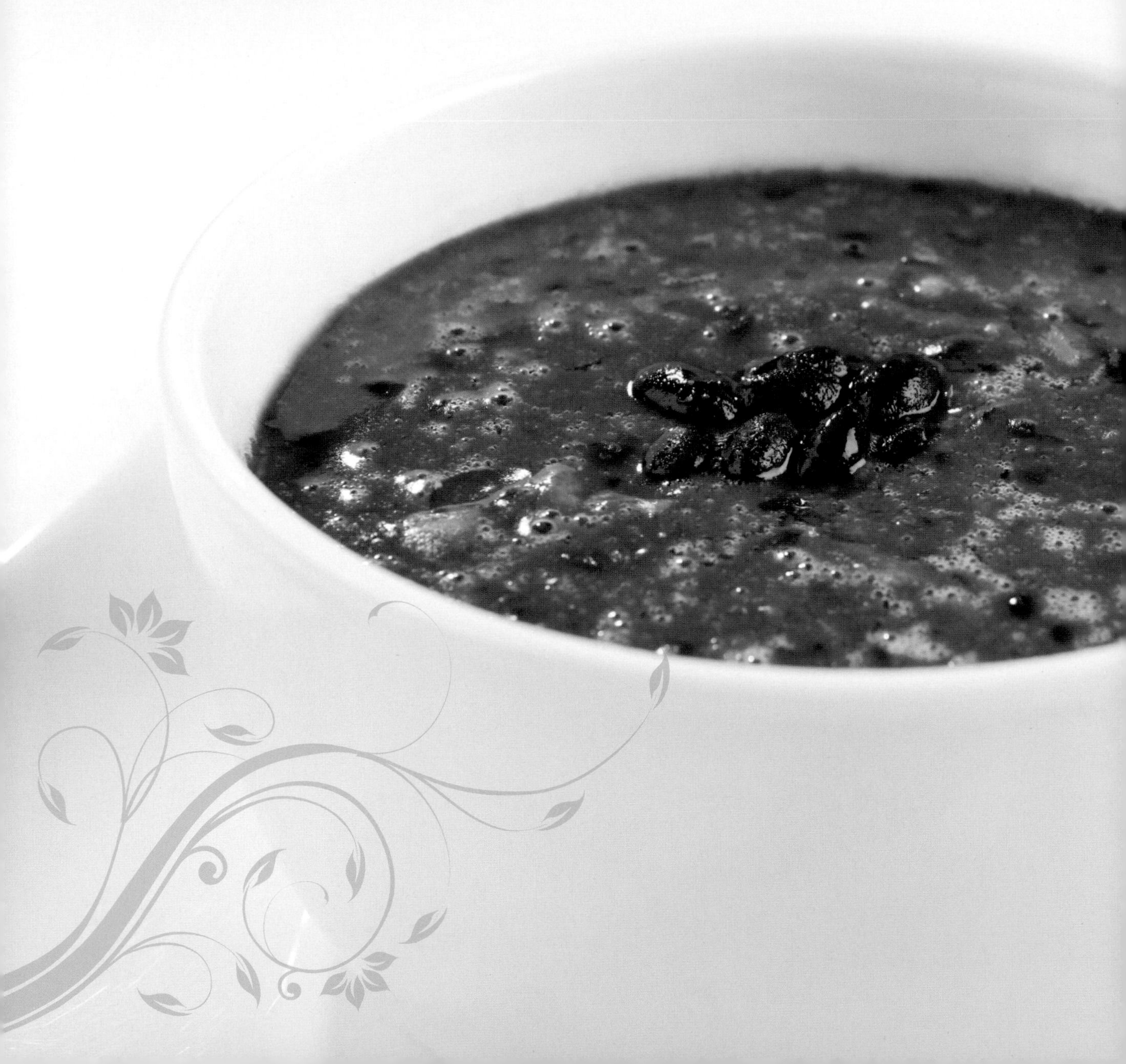

BLACK BEAN SOUP
SERVES 4

¼ cup white onion, diced
1 tablespoon coconut oil
3 cloves garlic, minced or
   pressed
1 teaspoon ground cumin
¼ teaspoon cayenne pepper
1 teaspoon sea salt
4 cups vegetable broth
4 cups cooked black beans

OPTIONAL TOPPINGS
¼ cup Daiya® cheddar
   shreds, optional
½ cup fresh cilantro

In a large stockpot over medium-high heat, sauté the onion in coconut oil for 2 minutes. Add the garlic and continue to cook for 1 to 2 minutes. Stir in the cumin, cayenne pepper, and sea salt. Add the broth and black beans. Cook, stirring occasionally, for 10 minutes. Transfer to a Vitamix in batches, if necessary, and process to desired consistency. I like it chunkier, or purée it until smooth. Top with cheddar shreds and cilantro, if desired.

Ⓥ Ⓟ ⒹⒻ ⒼⒻ ⓀⒻ

Homemade tortilla chips are the perfect accompaniment to my black bean soup. Cut your favorite gluten-free, corn-free tortillas into triangles, lightly coat with coconut oil, and bake in a preheated 350°F oven for 10 minutes, or until lightly browned and crisp.

what the symbols mean:
vegan • raw • paleo • dairy-free
gluten-free • kid friendly

V R P DF GF KF

CHEF V'S
SENSATIONAL SALADS

Green is good! Let me show you a variety of tasty ways you can create a sensational salad. Starting with fresh locally sourced organic greens, top your salad with a variety of colorful vegetables, fruits, legumes, and a touch of lean protein, drizzled with one of my delicious and healthy dressings. Salads are easy to prepare and are a super convenient way to get more nutrients into your diet. Research has shown that people who frequently eat green salads are likely to have higher blood levels of powerful antioxidants (Vitamin C and E, folic acid, and beta-carotene), especially if the salads include raw vegetables.

CHEF V'S CILANTRO LIME VINAIGRETTE

Chef V's Tip: Most of my salads are delicious with my Cilantro Lime Vinaigrette or Creamy Avocado Dressing. Use these on any salads unless otherwise specified. Dressings serve 4-6.

1 tablespoon fresh lime juice
1 tablespoon white vinegar
⅛ teaspoon sea salt
1 clove garlic, minced or pressed
2 tablespoons chopped fresh cilantro
2 tablespoons cold-pressed olive oil
2 tablespoons cold filtered water

Process all ingredients in a Vitamix until smooth and well combined. Will keep refrigerated in an airtight container for up to 1 week. Shake well before each use.

Ⓥ Ⓡ Ⓟ ⒹⒻ ⒼⒻ ⓀⒻ

CHEF V'S CREAMY AVOCADO DRESSING

1 large ripe avocado
½ small white onion, minced or grated
1 clove garlic, minced or pressed
1 small lime, juiced
1 tablespoon cold-pressed olive oil or avocado oil
1 teaspoon sea salt

Process all ingredients in a Vitamix until smooth and well combined. Serve immediately.

Ⓥ Ⓡ Ⓟ ⒹⒻ ⒼⒻ ⓀⒻ

EASY GREEN SALAD

SERVES 2

3 cups mixed greens (use
  your fav!)
1 cup shredded green
  cabbage
1 small seedless cucumber,
  peeled and sliced
1 cup cooked hot or cold
  kidney beans
1 ripe avocado, sliced

Gently combine all the
ingredients, drizzle with one
of my dressings, and serve.

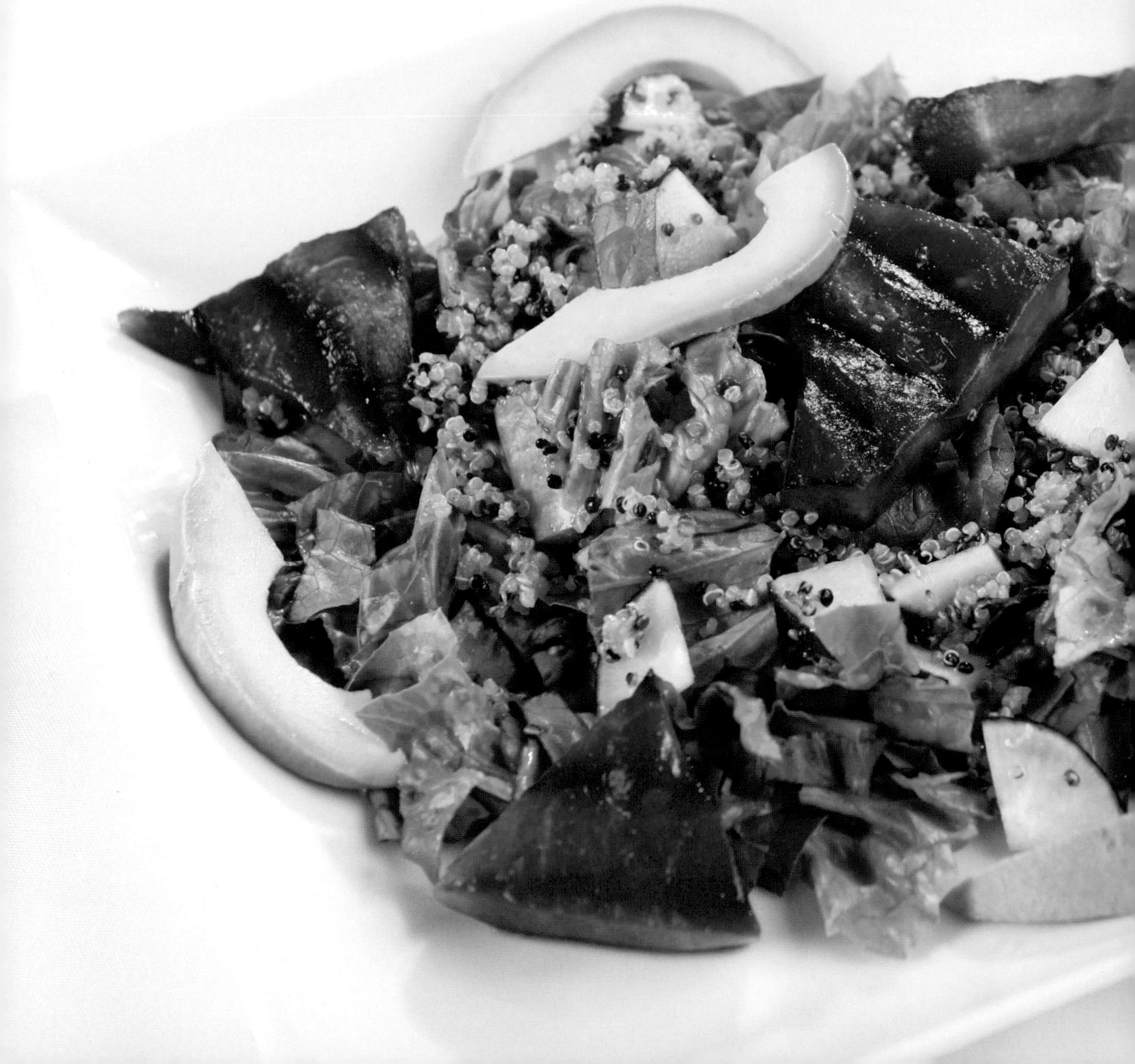

GRILLED WATERMELON + QUINOA SALAD

SERVES 2

2 (1-inch-thick) slices watermelon, seeded
3 cups cooked quinoa *(See tip, page36)*
3 radishes, sliced
⅔ cup Cilantro Lime Vinaigrette *(See recipe, page 82)*
10 cups chopped romaine lettuce
2 medium ripe avocados, sliced
¼ teaspoon chili powder, optional
2 tablespoons chopped fresh cilantro, optional

Preheat a grill or a grill pan on a stove over medium-high heat. Place the watermelon slices on the grill rack or pan and cook for about 4 minutes, or until the watermelon is lightly charred, turning once about halfway through cooking. Transfer to a cutting board and cut each watermelon piece into wedges.

In a large bowl, combine the quinoa and radish slices and lightly toss with the vinaigrette.

To serve, make a bed of the chopped lettuce on a large serving platter and top with the quinoa mixture. Next, arrange the watermelon slices and avocados, and sprinkle with chili powder and chopped cilantro. Serve with extra vinaigrette on the side.

SUPER FOOD POWER SALAD

SERVES 2

Chef V's Tip: One thing I like to do with kale is to squeeze fresh lemon juice on it and let it sit a few minutes. The acid in the juice helps to soften and wilt the greens, making them a little tastier.

1 lemon, juiced
4 cups chopped green
   kale or baby kale
1 ripe avocado, diced
½ cup pomegranate seeds
½ cup red kidney beans, drained
   and rinsed
Raw pine nuts, or use
   your fav!

Squeeze the lemon juice onto the chopped kale and let it sit a few minutes. Then mash the avocado into the greens. Sprinkle with pomegranate seeds, kidney beans, and your favorite nuts, and serve.

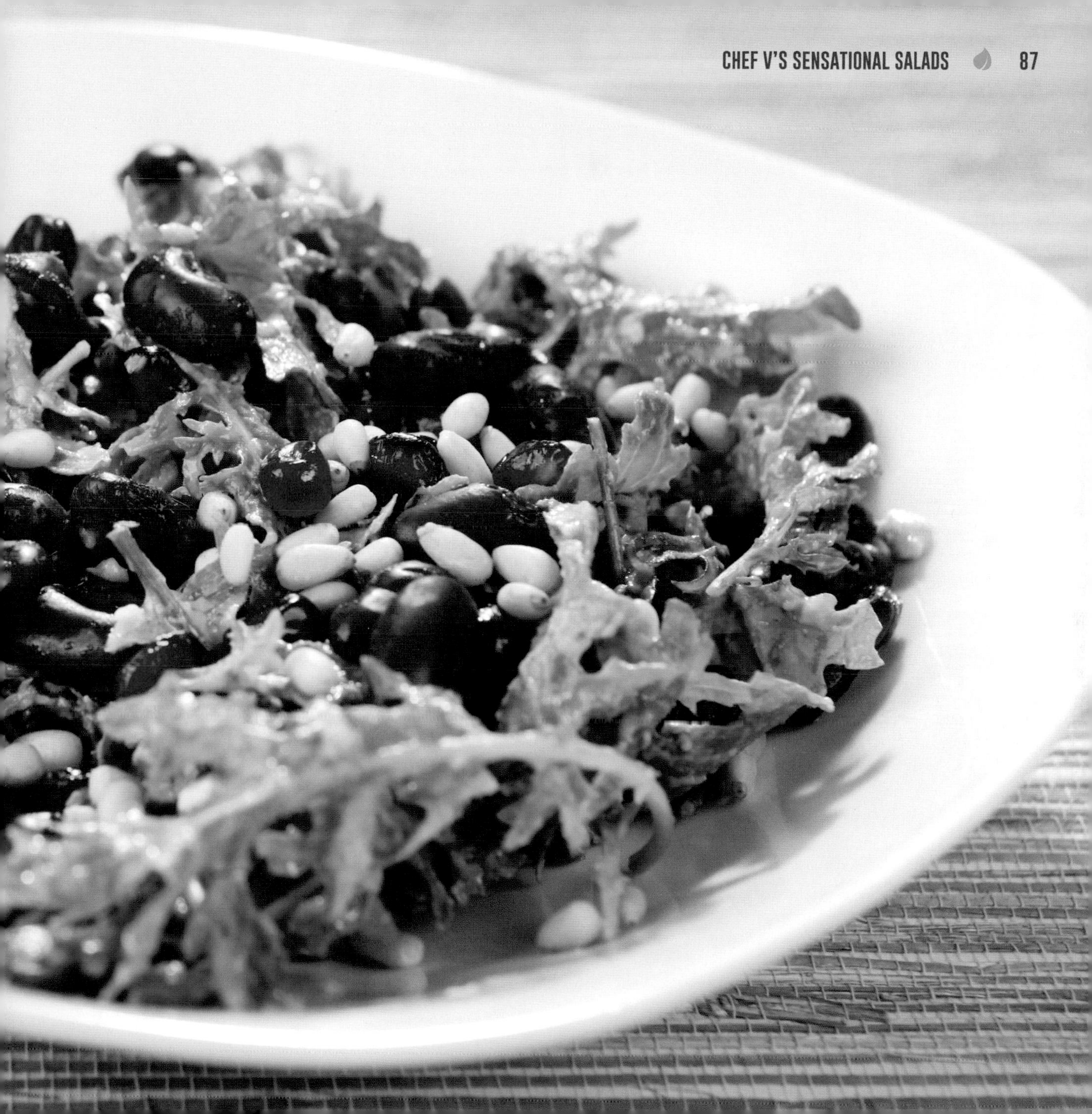

CHEF V'S ANTIOXIDANT LOVE SALAD
SERVES 2

- **1 tablespoon cold-pressed olive oil**
- **1 tablespoon balsamic vinegar**
- **1 large red chard leaf, chopped**
- **1 cup chopped red leaf lettuce**
- **1 small raw beet, grated**
- **½ cup raspberries**
- **¼ cup pomegranate seeds**
- **¼ cup raw walnuts, chopped**

In a bowl, toss the olive oil and vinegar with the greens. Plate and top with beets, raspberries, pomegranate seeds, and chopped walnuts.

Ⓥ Ⓡ Ⓟ ⒹⒻ ⒼⒻ

Pomegranate seeds are so yummy. They are sweet and tart and add a delicious crunch to any dish. They have lots of fiber and two essential Vitamins, C and K. Sprinkle them on your favorite salads and soups, or toss them into your next smoothie.

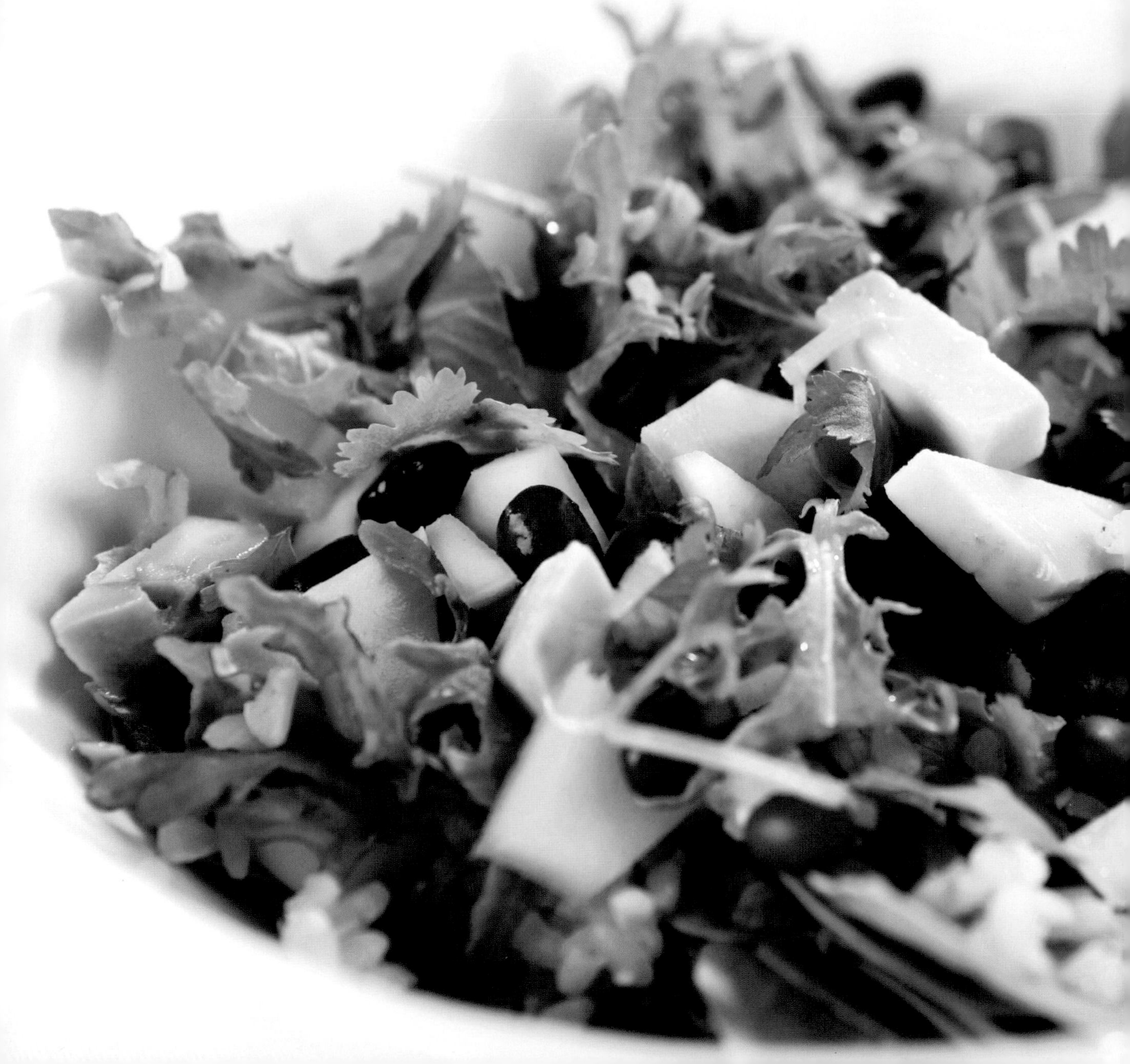

MANGO AVOCADO BURRITO BOWL
SERVES 2

Here's my spin on Chipotle® Mexican Grill's awesome burrito bowls. Use my recipe as a starting point and add any of your favorite ingredients like grilled chicken or fish to make this your own. You can also turn this into an easy wrap with gluten-free tortillas.

½ mango, peeled and diced
¼ cup chopped fresh cilantro
¼ small red onion, diced
1 small lime, juiced
2 cups mixed greens (use your fav!)
1 cup cooked brown rice or cauliflower
   cilantro rice *(See recipe, page 126)*
¾ cup cooked and cooled or
   1 (15 ounce) can black beans, drained
   and rinsed
½ ripe avocado, diced

In a small bowl, combine the mango, cilantro, red onion, and lime juice. Plate the greens, and top with brown rice or quinoa, black beans, mango mixture, and diced avocado. Serve. Ⓥ Ⓟ ⒹⒻ ⒼⒻ ⓀⒻ

SWEET WATERMELON CRUNCH SALAD

SERVES 2-4

Chef V's Tip: To blanch the broccoli, bring a pot of water to a boil, drop the broccoli in for 1 minute, and then remove and cool with ice water. This will make it slightly softer without losing much nutritional value.

SALAD

2 cups arugula
3 cups chopped watermelon, seeded
2 ripe Bartlett pears, peeled and thinly sliced
3 cups chopped broccoli florets, blanched and cooled
2 tablespoons raw pine nuts

ZESTY DRESSING

¼ cup cold-pressed olive oil
2 tablespoons apple cider vinegar
1 teaspoon Dijon or dry mustard
½ teaspoon lemon zest

Plate the greens with watermelon, pears, broccoli florets, and a sprinkling of pine nuts.

Combine the dressing ingredients. Drizzle over the salad and serve.

(V) (P) (DF) (GF) (KF)

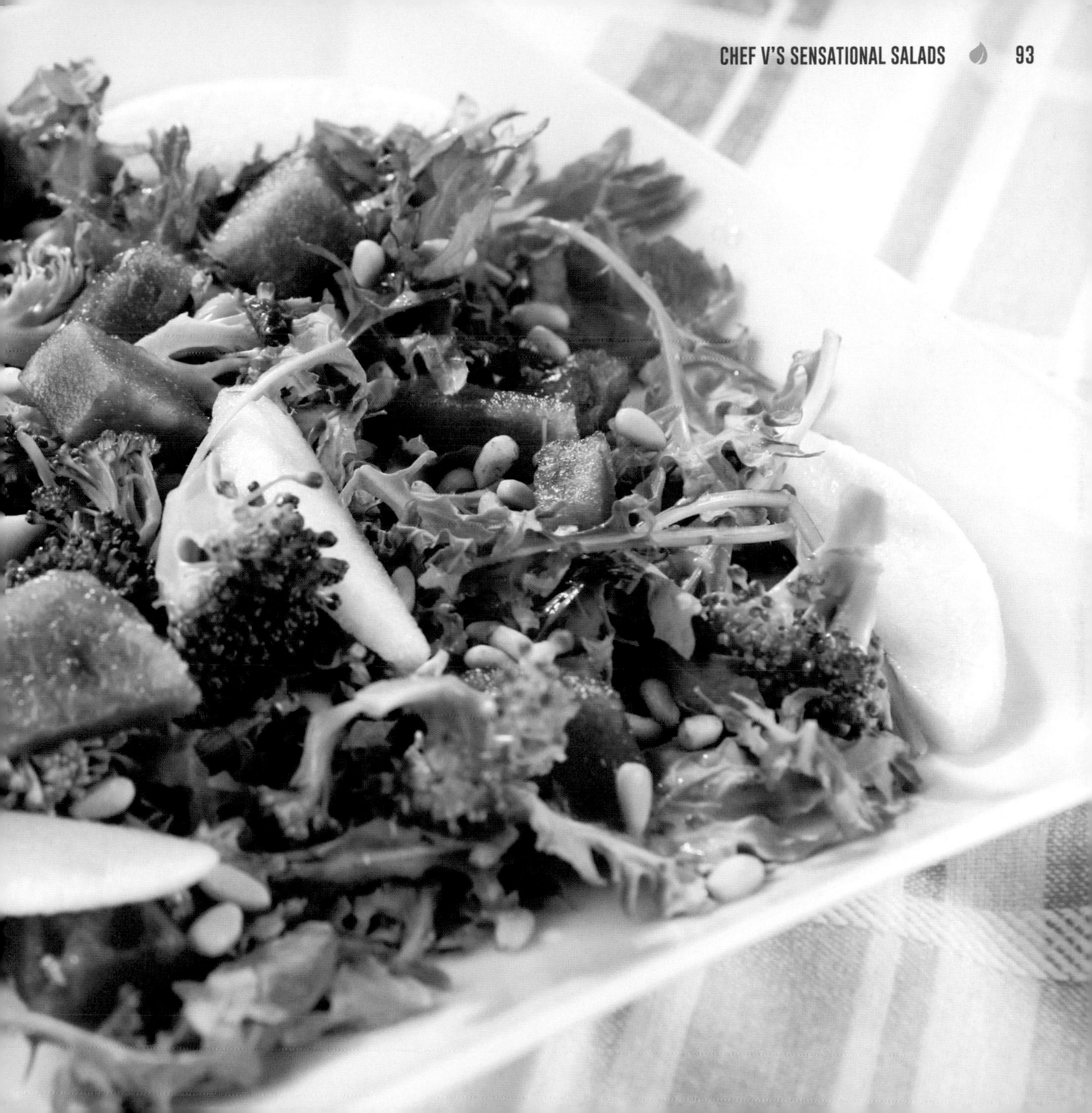

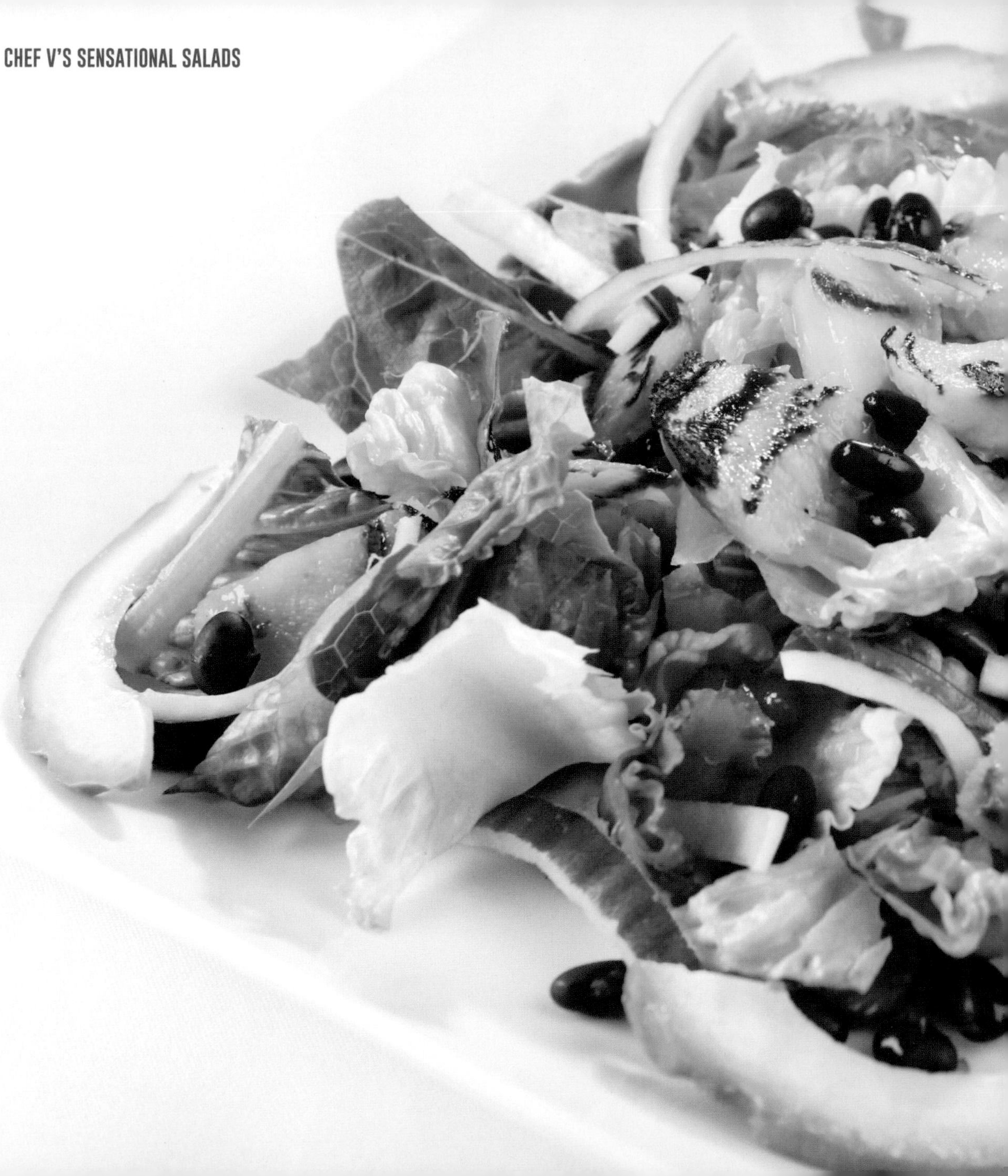

GRILLED MANGO SALAD

SERVES 4

Chef V's Tip: Add grilled chicken or fish for more protein!

**1 to 2 mangos, peeled and cut into
   thick slices**
4 cups mixed greens (use your fav!)
½ cup sliced red onion
**1 cup cooked and cooled or
   1 (15-ounce) can black beans,
   drained and rinsed**
1 avocado, diced
¼ cup Cilantro Lime Dressing
   (See recipe, page 81)

Preheat a grill or a grill pan on a stove over medium-high heat. Place the mango slices on the grill rack or pan and cook for 1 minute, or until grill marks appear. Transfer to a cutting board and cut the grilled mango into smaller chunks. Plate the greens and top with the grilled mango, red onion, and black beans. Drizzle with dressing and serve.

CHOPPED GREEK SALAD

SERVES 2-4

- 2 tablespoons cold-pressed olive oil
- 1 tablespoon apple cider vinegar
- 2 cups chopped romaine lettuce
- 1 large cucumber, peeled and cut into 1-inch slices
- 1 cup cooked garbanzo beans
- 1 tablespoon chopped fresh mint
- 1 tablespoon chopped fresh flat-leaf parsley
- 1 tablespoon chopped fresh basil
- ¼ cup Kalamata olives, seeded and cut in half

Chef V's Tip: I always use cold-pressed olive oil. Cold pressing is the process where the oil is produced through a combination of grinding and low heat. The introduction of heat to the process can degrade an oil's flavor, nutritional value, and color, and may expose the oil to toxins. So the lower processing temperatures of cold pressing help retain all the great benefits and taste of the oil.

In a bowl, toss the olive oil and vinegar with the romaine lettuce. Gently add in the remaining ingredients, refrigerate for 1 hour to marinate, and serve cold.

Ⓥ Ⓟ ⒹⒻ ⒼⒻ

I love the refreshing flavor that mint adds to dishes. There are so many varieties of mint — from the better known peppermint and spearmint to the more exotic and fun mojito mint, orange mint, chocolate mint, even a ginger mint! Mint promotes digestion and soothes stomachs in cases of indigestion or inflammation. Add mint to salads or soups, or brew up a tasty cup of mint tea.

WARM BUTTERNUT SQUASH SALAD

SERVES 4

1 tablespoon coconut oil

¼ cup diced sweet or yellow onion

1 small butternut squash, seeded and diced

1 clove garlic, minced or pressed

½ teaspoon freshly grated nutmeg

½ teaspoon fresh thyme leaves

1 cup cooked quinoa
(See tip, page 36)

Sea salt, to taste

Freshly ground black pepper

4 cups wild greens (arugula, spinach, or mixed herbs)

1 cup pomegranate seeds

DRESSING

¼ cup cold-pressed olive oil

1 tablespoon apple cider vinegar

Chef V's Tip: This is a delicious fall treat. It's very filling and makes you feel warm inside even though it's a salad. It's also very healthy and vegan. See my fail-proof way to cook quinoa on page 36.

In a large nonstick pan, heat the coconut oil over medium heat. Add the diced onion and butternut squash. (The smaller the squash is diced, the more quickly it will cook.) Sauté the squash and onions over medium heat for about 5 minutes, or until the squash is soft. Do not burn the squash or onions. Add the garlic, nutmeg, and thyme, and cook for 1 to 2 minutes more. Transfer the butternut squash to a bowl and stir in the cooked quinoa. Add salt and pepper to taste. Cool mixture in the refrigerator.

To serve, mix dressing ingredients and drizzle over greens. Top with cooled butternut squash mix and garnish with pomegranate seeds.

(V) (DF) (GF) (KF)

what the symbols mean:
vegan · raw · paleo · dairy-free
gluten-free · kid friendly

V R P DF GF KF

CHEF V'S
EASY ENTRÉES + SIDES

I love cooking for my family and experimenting with new recipes and new foods. And even though we all have busy lives, I still try nearly every night to head into the kitchen and make a healthy dinner (plus leftovers are great for lunch the next day). All of my recipes are organic, dairy-free, gluten-free, and a chock full of nutritious — and flavorful — ingredients. Your tastebuds will take a trip around the world — from the Far East to the Mediterranean and Mexico! You won't be bored creating these easy entrées and side dishes that you can mix and match.

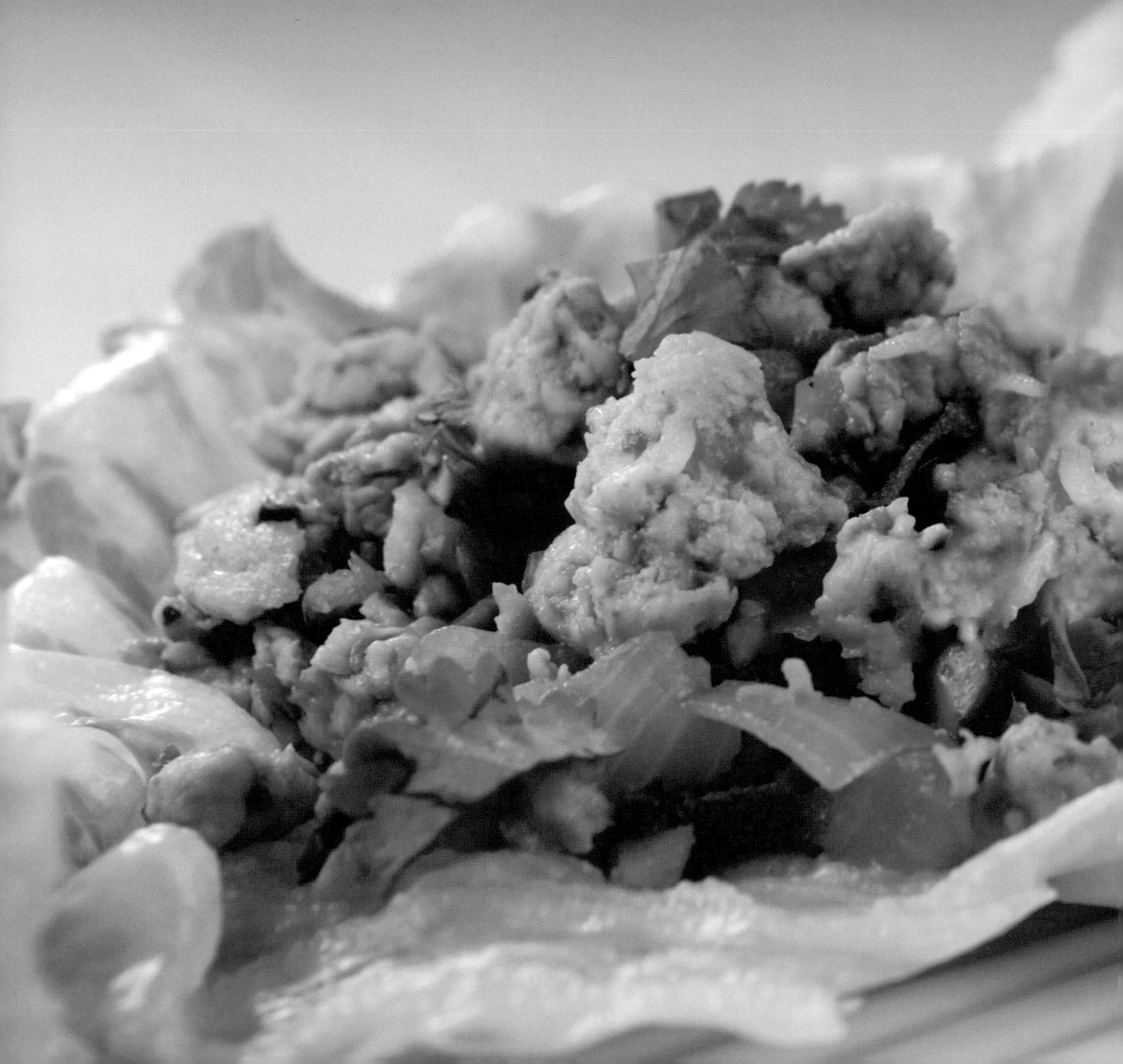

TASTY LETTUCE CUPS
SERVES 5-6

Chef V's Tip: For more protein, add 1 pound ground chicken. Raw coconut aminos are a fabulous replacement for soy sauce.

1 tablespoon coconut oil
½ cup diced white onion
2 cloves garlic, minced or pressed
2 cup diced crimini mushrooms
1 cup diced zucchini
½ cup diced water chestnuts
2 carrots, shredded
¼ cup raw coconut aminos (I like Coconut Secret®)
5-6 lettuce cups (iceberg or boston lettuce leaves)

OPTIONAL TOPPINGS
¼ cup chopped cilantro
¼ cup chopped raw cashews

In a large skillet, sauté onion in coconut oil over medium-high heat for 2 minutes. Add garlic and cook for 1 minute, then add mushrooms and veggies (or ground chicken) and cook for 3 more minutes. Stir in coconut aminos and cook for 2 minutes more.

To serve, spoon mixture into lettuce cups. Top with cilantro and cashews. Ⓥ Ⓟ DF GF KF

MACHO NACHOS
SERVES 2-4

Chef V's Tip: For more protein, use 1 pound ground turkey instead of mushrooms. This is great for entertaining!

CHEF V'S TACO SEASONING

2 teaspoons hot chili powder
1 teaspoon of each: paprika and onion powder
½ teaspoon of each: sea salt, garlic powder,
   ground cumin, and oregano
¼ teaspoon black pepper
⅛ teaspoon of each: cayenne pepper and
   red pepper flakes

TORTILLA CHIPS

4 gluten-free, corn-free tortillas (I like Rudi's®)
1 tablespoon coconut oil
1 teaspoon Chef V's Taco Seasoning
½ cup shredded Daiya® cheddar shreds

NACHO 'MEAT'

1 tablespoon coconut oil
½ cup diced yellow onion
2 cups diced mushrooms or 1 pound ground turkey
1 tablespoon Chef V's Taco Seasoning
¼ cup water or Chef V's Raw Almond Milk
   (See recipe, page 32)

TOPPINGS

1 cup cooked or canned black or pinto beans, warmed
1 whole avocado, diced
½ cup of each: diced and peeled mango, chopped
   cilantro, and chopped green onion

Combine all taco seasoning ingredients in a small bowl. Set aside.

Preheat oven to 350°F. Cut the tortillas into chip shapes. In a large bowl, combine the coconut oil and 1 teaspoon of taco seasoning, if desired. Add the chips and gently coat. Line 1 or 2 baking sheets with foil or parchment paper or use an oven-safe serveware piece. Place the chips in a single layer. Bake for 8-10 minutes, but do not completely cook the chips. Remove the chips from the oven and sprinkle with Daiya® shreds. Bake for 3-4 more minutes, until the shreds are melted.

To make the nacho 'meat,' melt the coconut oil over medium-high heat in a saucepan. Add the onions and sauté until translucent, about 2-3 minutes. Stir in the mushrooms (or ground turkey) and cook for 3 minutes. Add the taco seasoning and water or almond milk. Continue to cook through, stirring occasionally, for 2-3 more minutes. Keep warm on the stovetop.

To serve, transfer the chips onto a serving plate or leave on the oven-safe serveware piece. Top with warm black beans or pinto beans, nacho 'meat' (vegan or turkey), avocado, mango, cilantro, and green onion.

(V) (DF) (GF) (KF)

SEARED AHI TUNA
SERVES 2 AS AN ENTREÉ OR 4 AS AN APPETIZER

Chef V's Tip: This is great to dip in a little dish of raw coconut aminos. Serve with a side of my Easy Fried Rice (See recipe, page 125) or my Spicy Sweet Potato Purée (See recipe, page 127).

2 lemons, juiced
2 tablespoons cold-pressed olive oil, divided use
2 tablespoons freshly ground rainbow peppercorns
1 pound sushi-grade ahi tuna steak
1 teaspoon black sesame seeds
1 teaspoon white sesame seeds
¼ cup chopped fresh flat-leaf parsley, for garnish
Pink sea salt, optional, for garnish
Lemon slices

Mix the lemon juice and 1 tablespoon of oil in one shallow dish and place the freshly ground peppercorns in another. Coat the tuna steak in the lemon juice, then with the peppercorns and the sesame seeds.

Heat the remaining oil in a large pan over high heat. Once the oil is hot, sear the tuna for 30 seconds on each side. Remove the tuna and let it sit for 1 to 2 minutes before slicing into ¼-inch pieces. To serve, plate the tuna slices, sprinkle with sea salt and chopped parsley, and top with lemon slices. **P** **DF** **GF**

GINGER GLAZED SALMON + BOK CHOY
SERVES 2

Chef V's Note: Try this with any of your other favorite fish fillets.

1 tablespoon cold-pressed olive oil
2 tablespoons coconut aminos
1 lemon, juiced
2 cloves garlic, minced or pressed
2 teaspoons fresh ginger, minced or pressed
2 (6-ounce) wild salmon fillets
2 baby bok choy
Sea salt, optional to taste

Mix the olive oil, coconut aminos, lemon juice, garlic, and ginger in bowl. Divide the marinade between 2 shallow dishes or zip-top bags and place the salmon in one and the bok choy in the other. Marinate both for 30 minutes.

Heat a grill or grill pan and grill the salmon for 5 minutes per side, or until cooked to desired doneness. Grill the baby bok choy until lightly charred, 1-2 minutes per side, or until tender. Brush with extra marinade while grilling. **P** **DF** **GF** **KF**

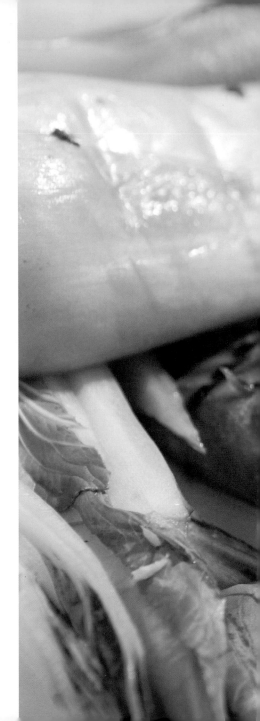

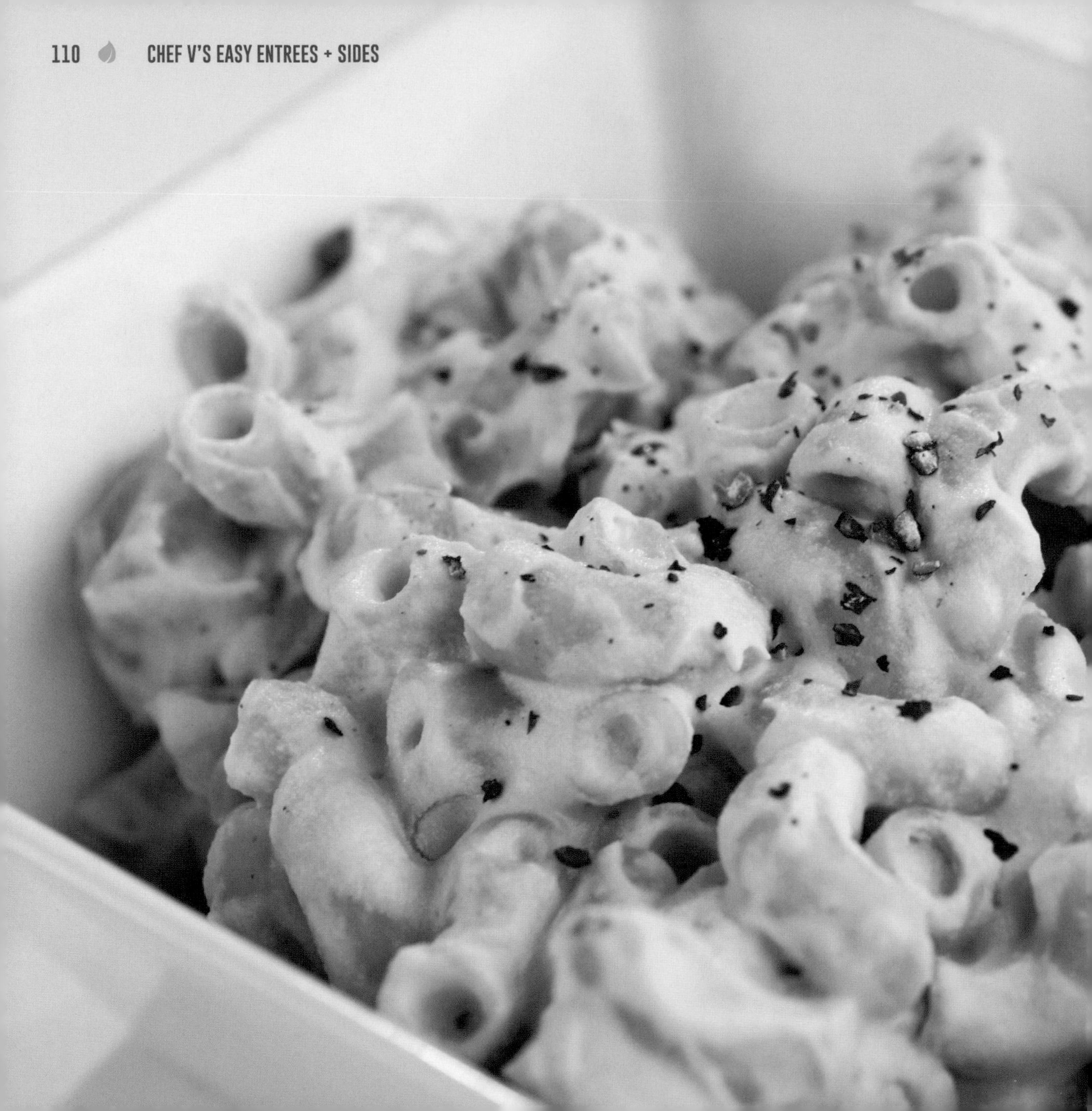

AWESOME MAC + 'CHEESE'
SERVES 2-4

Chef V's Tip: This is my gluten-free, dairy-free version of macaroni and cheese.

3 cups filtered water
2 cups peeled and chopped butternut squash
½ cup Chef V's Raw Almond Milk *(See recipe, page 32)*
1 clove garlic, minced or pressed
2 cups raw cashews, soaked and drained *(See tip, page 35)*
½ lemon, juiced
¼ teaspoon sea salt
2 cups cooked brown rice elbow pasta
Freshly ground black pepper, optional

Bring the 3 cups of water to a boil in a saucepan and cook the butternut squash for 20 to 30 minutes, or until soft. Process the cooked squash, almond milk, garlic, cashews, lemon juice, and salt in a Vitamix until smooth. Combine the 'cheese' sauce and cooked pasta, season with black pepper, if desired, and serve. **V** **DF** **GF** **KF**

CHEF V'S FOOD FACT:
BUTTERNUT SQUASH, LIKE ALL MEMBERS OF THE GOURD FAMILY (INCLUDING MELONS, PUMPKINS, AND CUCUMBERS), IS TECHNICALLY A FRUIT BECAUSE IT HAS SEEDS. WITH A MILDLY SWEET AND NUTTY FLAVOR, IT IS A NUTRITIONAL HEAVY HITTER — RICH IN FIBER, PHYTONUTRIENTS, AND ANTIOXIDANTS.

PESTO LASAGNA WITH MACADAMIA 'RICOTTA'
SERVES 2

'RICOTTA CHEESE'
1 cup macadamia nuts, soaked for an hour *(See tip, page 35)*
1 lemon, juiced
1 tablespoon cold-pressed olive oil
1 teaspoon sea salt
1 tablespoon fresh rosemary

PESTO
1 cup fresh basil
½ cup raw pine nuts
1 clove garlic, minced or pressed
2 tablespoons filtered water
½ cup arugula
1 teaspoon sea salt
2 tablespoons cold-pressed olive oil

'NOODLES'
4 large zucchini, sliced thin length-wise
2 large portobello mushrooms, sliced thin

GARNISHES
Raw pine nuts
Fresh julienned basil

Chef V's Tips: This is my raw version of traditional lasagna. I replace pasta noodles with sliced zucchini and portobello mushrooms, and a delicious nut and rosemary mixture takes the place of the usual cheese. You can prepare this in a 3x8-inch baking dish or 2 individual bowls or dishes.

Make the 'ricotta' by processing all the 'cheese' ingredients in a Vitamix until smooth. Transfer to a bowl and set aside.

Clean the Vitamix and add all the pesto ingredients except the olive oil. Slowly add the oil while processing. Transfer to a bowl and set aside.

To assemble the lasagna:
Step 1: Spoon a small amount of pesto over the bottom of the baking dish.
Step 2: Layer 2 to 3 pieces of zucchini. (If creating individual servings, you may need to cut the vegetables into smaller strips.)
Step 3: Layer ½ of the 'cheese' on top.
Step 4: Layer 2 to 3 portobello mushrooms.
Step 5: Top with ½ of the pesto. Repeat steps 2-5 once, ending with the pesto layer on top. Garnish with leftover pine nuts and shredded basil.

Enjoy raw or bake in a 350°F oven for 20 minutes for a warm version.   (V) (R) (P) (DF) (GF) (KF)

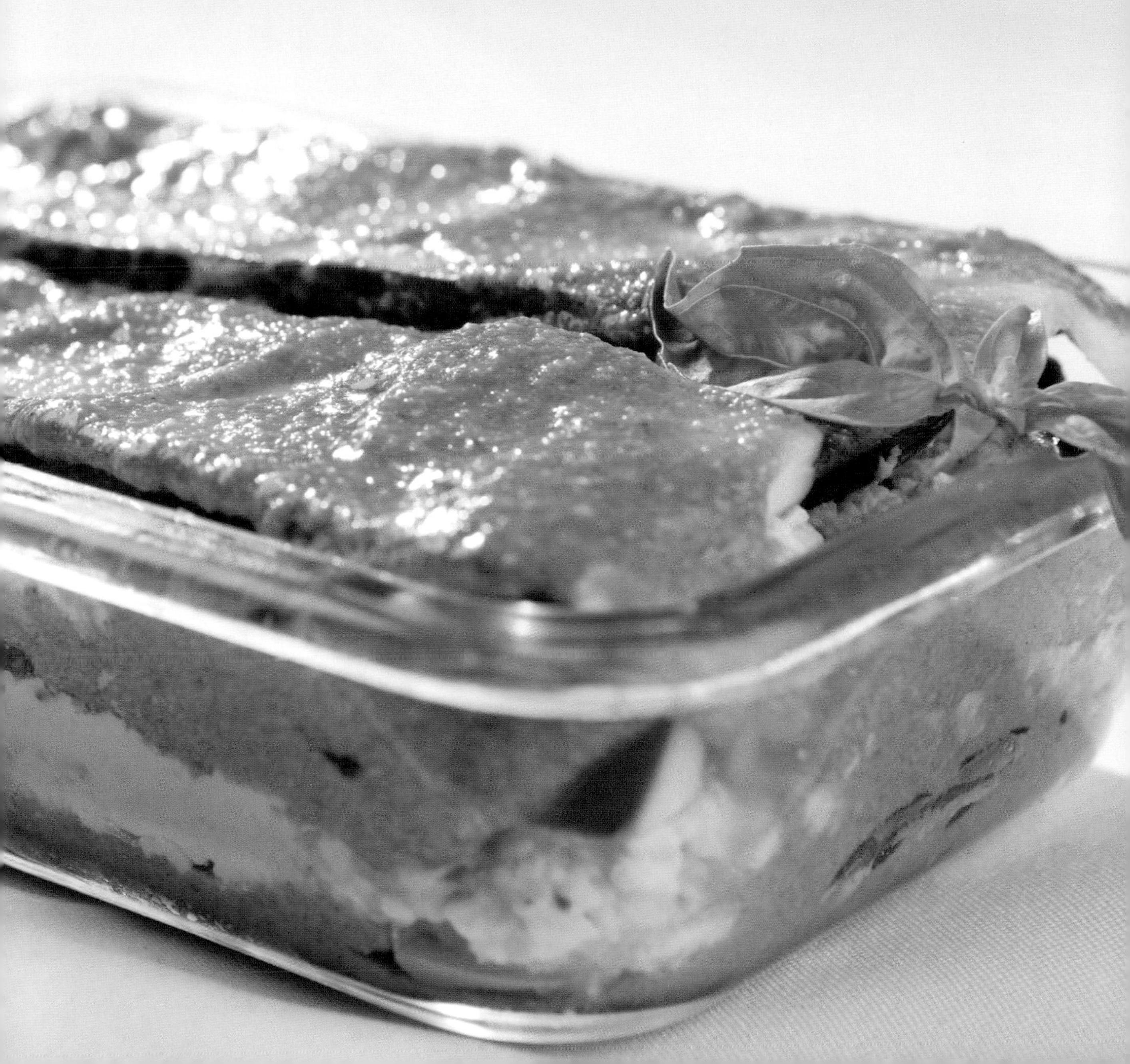

GRILLED CHICKEN PESTO PASTA

SERVES 2

Sea salt and freshly
  ground black
  pepper, to taste
1 pound boneless,
  skinless chicken
  breast
2 cups cooked brown
  rice or quinoa pasta
½ cup Chef V's Easy
  Raw Pesto *(below)*

*Chef V's Tip: Substitute the chicken with
2 cups of your favorite grilled veggies to
make this dish vegan.*

Preheat a grill or grill pan to medium-
high. Lightly salt and pepper the chicken
(or veggies) and grill for 3 to 5 minutes
on each side, or until thoroughly cooked.
Cut chicken into pieces and combine
with cooked pasta and my easy pesto.

(DF) (GF) (KF)

CHEF V'S EASY RAW PESTO

SERVES 8

2 cups fresh basil
¾ cup raw pine nuts
2 cloves garlic
½ cup cold-pressed
  olive oil
1 tablespoon fresh lemon
  juice
Sea salt and freshly
  ground black pepper,
  to taste

*Chef V's Tip: This raw pesto is so
delicious. Besides my Grilled Chicken
Pasta, try this on gluten-free bread as a
spread or use it as a marinade for your
favorite protein or vegetables.*

Process all of the ingredients in a
Vitamix until smooth. Will keep for up
to a week refrigerated.

MOUSSAKA
SERVES ABOUT 4

Chef V's Tip: For a vegan version, replace ground lamb with 3 cups minced mushrooms.

2 tablespoons cold-pressed olive oil, divided use
¼ cup diced white onion
1 clove garlic, minced or pressed
1 pound ground lamb
1 tablespoon gluten-free flour
1 cup Chef V's Raw Almond Milk, room temperature *(See recipe, page 32)*
¾ cup Daiya® mozzarella shreds, divided use
½ cup vegetable broth
½ teaspoon dried rosemary
⅛ teaspoon ground nutmeg
Sea salt and black pepper, to taste
1 large (or 2 small) zucchini, thinly sliced lengthwise like lasagna noodles

Preheat oven to 350°F. Lightly coat a 6x6-inch baking dish with coconut oil spray. Set aside.

In a nonstick skillet, sauté the onions in 1 tablespoon of oil for 2 minutes. Stir in the garlic and lamb (and/or mushrooms). Sauté for 3 more minutes, until the lamb is cooked and mushrooms are soft but still have texture. Set aside.

Heat the remaining oil in a small saucepan over medium-low heat. Add the flour and whisk until it is completely incorporated. Let the flour cook for 1 more minute. Slowly whisk in the almond milk and cook for a few minutes, stirring occasionally. Add ½ cup of shreds and whisk until completely melted. Add veggie broth, rosemary, nutmeg, sea salt, and black pepper, and continue cooking until the sauce thickens, stirring occasionally.

Assemble the moussaka in the prepared baking dish:
Step 1: Cover the bottom with a layer of zucchini slices.
Step 2: Sprinkle with half of the mozzarella shreds.
Step 3: Top with lamb and/or mushroom mixture.
Step 4: Sprinkle remaining mozzarella shreds.
Step 5: Cover with a layer of zucchini slices.
Step 6: Top with sauce.

Bake for 45 minutes, or until the sauce is golden brown. Let cool for 10-15 minutes before serving. (P) (DF) (GF) (KF)

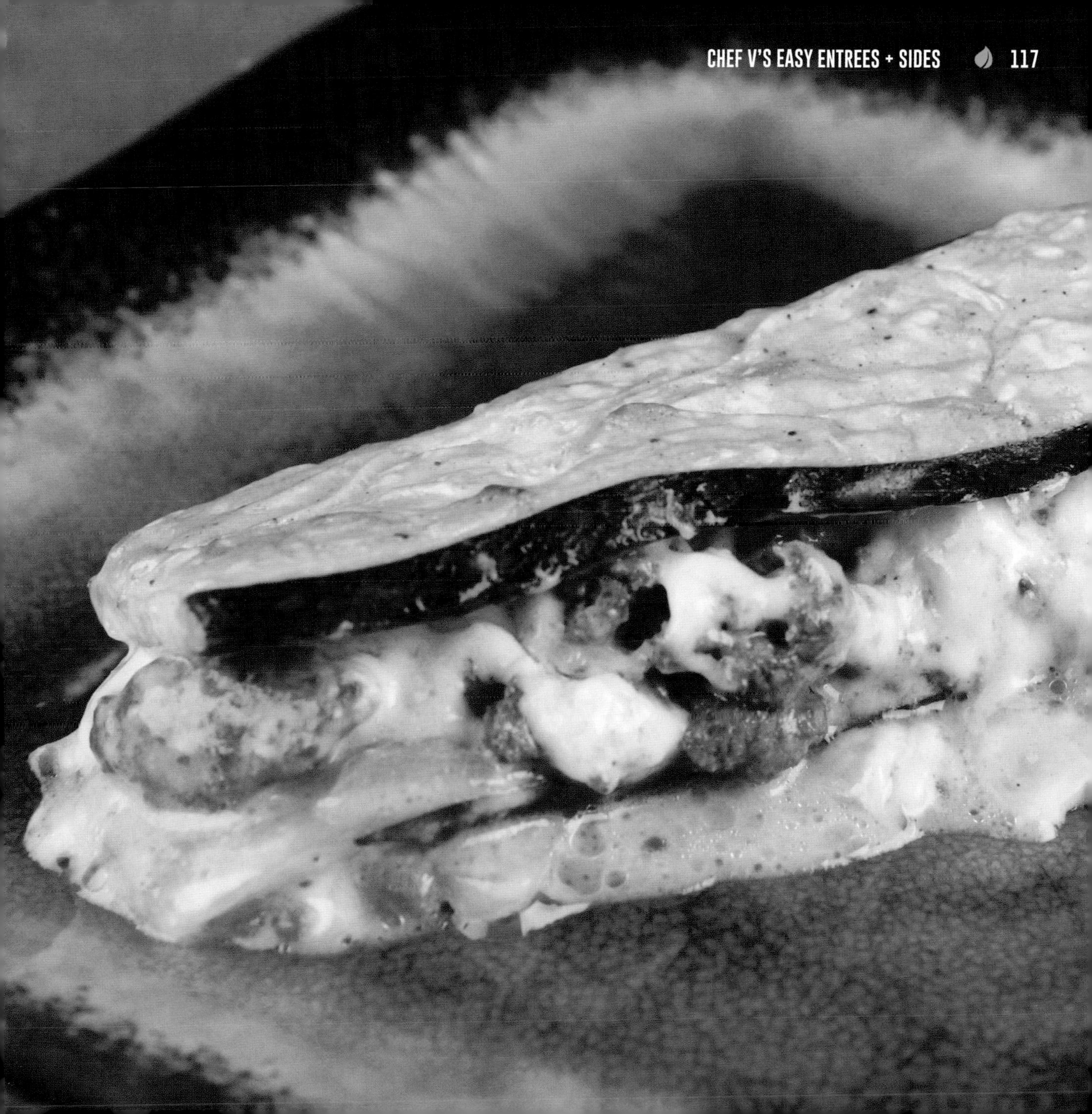

AVOCADO GREEN CURRY

SERVES 2

Chef V's Tip: For more protein add, 1 pound chopped grilled chicken. This dish is great with brown rice.

1 clove garlic, minced or pressed
1 tablespoon coconut oil
½ cup green beans
1 large zucchini, sliced into thin rounds
2 tablespoons green curry paste (I like Thai Kitchen®)
1 cup coconut milk
2 large ripe avocados, diced
½ cup fresh basil, julienned
Cooked brown rice or cooked quinoa

In a large saucepan, sauté the garlic in the coconut oil for 1 minute. Add the green beans and zucchini, and cook for 3 minutes. Stir in the curry paste, making sure to coat all of the vegetables. Slowly add the coconut milk and bring to a simmer for 3 minutes. Gently stir in avocado and basil and turn off the heat. Serve over brown rice or quinoa, optional.

THAI RED CURRY

SERVES 2

Chef V's Tip: For more protein, add 1 pound cooked boneless, skinless chicken breast pieces. This dish is great served with brown rice.

¼ cup sliced yellow onion
1 tablespoon cold-pressed olive oil
1 clove garlic, minced or pressed
½ cup snap peas
1 large carrot, thinly sliced
1 (8-ounce) can bamboo shoots, drained
1 pound zucchini, celery, or your favorite veggie,
   diced or thinly sliced
1 or 2 tablespoons red curry paste, to taste
   (I like Thai Kitchen®)
1 can light coconut milk
Sea salt and freshly ground black pepper, to taste
¼ cup fresh cilantro, chopped

In a large pot, sauté the onion in 1 tablespoon of oil over medium heat for 2 to 3 minutes, or until translucent. Add the garlic, snap peas, and carrot along with any of your other favorite veggies. Reduce heat to medium-low and cook for 2 more minutes, or until the veggies have just a bit of crunch. Add the bamboo shoots (and cooked chicken, if using) and stir in the curry paste, coating all the vegetables. Reduce the heat to low and stir in the coconut milk. Simmer for 5 minutes. Season with sea salt and freshly ground pepper to taste. Garnish with fresh cilantro.

(V) (P) (DF) (GF)

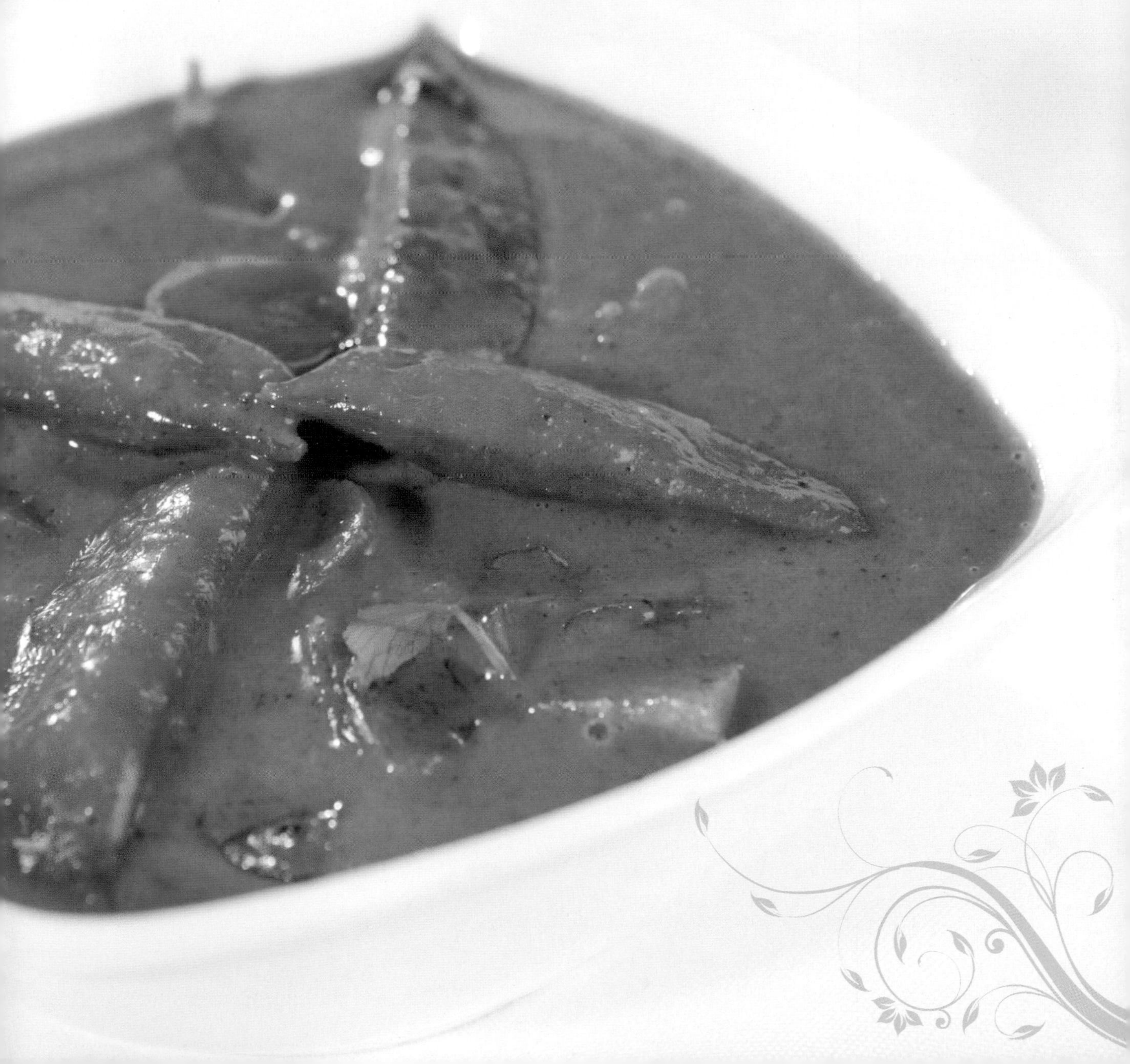

GRILLED ARTICHOKE

SERVES 2

6 cups filtered water
1 large fresh artichoke
2 cloves garlic, peeled
½ white onion
½ lemon, juiced
1 teaspoon apple cider vinegar
Sea salt and freshly ground
**   black pepper, to taste**

Bring the 6 cups of water to boil in a stockpot.

Trim the thorns from the artichoke leaves with scissors. Cut the artichoke in half vertically and remove the fuzzy center. To the boiling water, add the artichoke, garlic, and onion. Boil, covered, for about 30 to 45 minutes, or until the leaves pull out easily. Transfer the artichoke halves to a paper towel cut side down to drain the water.

Heat a grill or grill pan. Place the artichokes cut side down on the hot grill or grill pan and char for 2 to 3 minutes, or until you get good grill marks. This will add a nice smokiness. Plate the artichoke halves cut side up. In a small bowl, whisk the lemon juice and vinegar, drizzle over the artichoke, sprinkle with sea salt and pepper, and serve with Chef V's Raw Horseradish Mayo.

CHEF V'S RAW HORSERADISH MAYO

Chef V's Tip: Enjoy this as a dip with the grilled artichoke or other veggies or as a spread on gluten-free bread or wraps.

1 cup raw cashews, soaked for 1 hour and drained *(See tip, page 35)*
1 cup filtered water
¼ cup lemon juice

1 tablespoon lemon zest
½ teaspoon sea salt
1 teaspoon raw coconut sugar
1 tablespoon horseradish

Process all ingredients in a Vitamix until smooth.

EASY FRIED RICE
SERVES 2

Chef V's Tip: For more protein, add 1 pound chopped grilled chicken. This is a great side or a meal itself.

**1 pound mixed veggies (use your favs!),
  lightly salted**
½ cup diced yellow onion
2 tablespoons coconut oil, divided use
2 cloves garlic, minced or pressed
2 cups cooked brown rice
**2 tablespoons raw coconut aminos, divided use
  (I like Coconut Secret®)**
½ cup pineapple, diced
¼ cup chopped cilantro
1 teaspoon red pepper flakes, optional

Spray a grill or grill pan with coconut oil cooking spray. Cook veggies for 3-5 minutes per side, until done. Remove from grill, cut into 1-inch pieces, and set aside.

Sauté onions in 1 tablespoon of oil over medium-high heat for 3-4 minutes, or until translucent. Add garlic, remaining oil, and cooked rice. Cook for 1-2 minutes, then stir in 1 tablespoon of coconut aminos. Continue to cook for 1 more minute. Slowly stir in the remaining coconut aminos, diced pineapple, and grilled veggies (or grilled chicken). Cook for 2 minutes. Stir in cilantro and red pepper flakes, if desired. Remove from heat, plate, and serve hot. (V) (DF) (GF) (KF)

CILANTRO 'RICE'

SERVES 2-4

Chef V's Tip: If you are looking for a great replacement for grains, try this tasty side dish.

1 head cauliflower
2 cloves garlic, minced or pressed
1 tablespoon coconut oil
1-2 limes, juiced (about
 ¼ cup)
¼ cup chopped cilantro
Sea salt, to taste

Wash, carefully dry, and chop the cauliflower into pieces. This is essential for the proper consistency of the 'rice.' Place the cauliflower in a Vitamix and slowly pulse. The texture should look like short-grain rice. You may have to do this in batches to avoid it becoming mushy. In a saucepan, sauté the garlic in the oil over medium-high heat for 1 minute. Add the 'rice' and cook for 3-5 minutes, or until done. Pour the lime juice over the rice and gently stir in the cilantro. Season with sea salt. Serve warm.

SWEET POTATO PURÉE

SERVES 2

1 large sweet potato, peeled and chopped
3 cups filtered water
¼ cup Chef V's Raw Almond Milk *(See recipe, page 32),* or coconut milk
¼ teaspoon sea salt
¼ teaspoon cayenne pepper, optional
¼ teaspoon red pepper flakes, optional

Boil the sweet potato pieces in the 3 cups of water in a large pot for 15 minutes, or until soft. Transfer the pieces to a Vitamix and add the milk, sea salt, cayenne, and red pepper flakes, and process until smooth. Serve immediately or keep refrigerated for up to 1 week.

GREEN BEANS WITH ALMONDS

SERVES 1

1 teaspoon coconut oil
1 tablespoon slivered raw almonds
1 clove garlic, minced or pressed
½ cup fresh green beans, trimmed
1 teaspoon raw coconut aminos

In a skillet, heat the coconut oil over medium-high. Add the almonds and garlic, and stir to coat. Add the green beans and stir-fry for 1 to 2 minutes. Add the coconut aminos and cook for another 1 to 2 minutes. Serve warm.

what the symbols mean:
vegan • raw • paleo • dairy-free
gluten-free • kid friendly

CHEF V'S
SWEETS + TREATS

Living healthy doesn't mean having to deprive yourself of yummy desserts. You just need to indulge properly! I love treating myself, so I developed these recipes using good-for-you ingredients. You'll banish all the bad stuff forever once you taste my raw, gluten-free, dairy-free, egg-free desserts. I am sure you will be wowed by my vegan versions of traditional 'cheese' cake and a vanilla 'milk' shake. Even though these desserts are cleanse-approved, some of them are high in sugar (naturally), so enjoy them in moderation.

TRIPLE LAYER 'CHEESE' CAKE

SERVES 4-6

CRUST

1 cup raw slivered almonds

1 cup raw walnuts

1 cup pitted dates, soaked in
    water overnight and drained

¼ teaspoon sea salt

1 teaspoon pure vanilla extract

'CHEESE' CAKE

3 cups raw cashews, soaked and
    drained *(See tip, page 35)*

¼ cup coconut oil

¼ cup raw coconut nectar
    (I like Coconut Secret®)

1 teaspoon pure vanilla extract

½ lemon, juiced

TOP LAYER

1 cup pitted dates, soaked in
    water overnight and drained

3 tablespoons raw coconut
    nectar (I like Coconut Secret®)

2 tablespoons unsalted
    raw almond butter

¼ teaspoon sea salt

2 tablespoons coconut oil

1½ teaspoons pure vanilla
    extract

Chef V's Tips: This is my interpretation of a New York cheesecake. I've swapped the traditional cream cheese for a delicious mixture of cashews, coconut, and vanilla. You will need to make this cake in 2 steps, and give yourself 24 hours to complete it, since you will need to soak the cashews for at least 2 hours or overnight and will need freezing time for the cake as well. First, make the crust and the 'cheese' cake layers at the same time. Once those steps are complete, place the cake in the freezer for 4 hours or overnight. The final step is to make the topping and pour it over the chilled cake. You can serve the 'cheese' cake immediately, or refrigerate it for up to a week. But I recommend eating it now!

Coat an 8-inch springform pan with coconut oil or cold-pressed olive oil spray. Process the crust ingredients in a Vitamix until combined but not completely smooth. Leave some nutty texture. Spread this evenly across the bottom of the pan.

Next, process the 'cheese' cake ingredients in the Vitamix until completely smooth. Spread this evenly over the crust and place the pan in the freezer for at least 4 hours or overnight.

When ready to serve, process the top layer ingredients in a Vitamix until completely smooth. Remove the cheesecake from the freezer and from the springform pan. Pour and spread the topping evenly over the cake, cut into slices, and serve as is or garnish with fresh berries. Ⓥ Ⓡ Ⓟ ⒹⒻ ⒼⒻ ⓀⒻ

AÇAI BOWL
SERVES 1-2

Chef V's Tip: Try this for breakfast, too!

**1 frozen unsweetened açai smoothie packet
(I like Sambazon®)**
½ cup frozen blueberries
½ cup frozen raspberries or blackberries
½ cup Chef V's Raw Almond Milk
(See recipe, page 32)
**½ cup fresh seasonal fruit (blueberries,
raspberries, kiwi, peaches), use your favs!**
**1 tablespoon shredded unsweetened
coconut**
¼ cup crushed raw almonds, optional

In a Vitamix, process frozen açai juice,
blueberries, raspberries, and almond milk
on medium for 2-3 minutes, until smooth.
Transfer to a bowl and top with your favorite
fresh fruit, coconut, and almonds, if desired.

**CHEF V'S FOOD FACT:
THE AÇAI BERRY IS A GRAPE-LIKE
FRUIT NATIVE TO THE RAIN FORESTS
OF THE AMAZON. AÇAI BERRIES
CONTAIN ANTIOXIDANTS, FIBER,
AND HEART-HEALTHY FATS.**

CHIA SEED PUDDING
SERVES 2-4

1 cup chia seeds
2½ cups Chef V's Raw Almond Milk
  (See recipe, page 32)
1 tablespoon raw coconut nectar
  (I like Coconut Secret®)
1 teaspoon pure vanilla extract
½ teaspoon ground cinnamon,
  optional
Pinch sea salt

OPTIONAL TOPPINGS

Fresh fruit, dried fruit, shredded
  unsweetened coconut, raw nuts

Chef V's Tip: Chia Seed Pudding is also great for breakfast!

Place all of the ingredients except for toppings in a bowl and stir until well combined. Let the mixture sit for 5 minutes, then stir with a fork. Repeat this process every 5 minutes for about 30 minutes, or until the chia seeds have soaked up all the liquid. Chill pudding for 2 hours before serving. Top with your favorite garnish and dig in.

Ⓥ Ⓡ Ⓟ ⒹⒻ ⒼⒻ ⓀⒻ

CHEF V'S FOOD FACT:
CHIA SEEDS ARE TINY SUPERFOOD HEROES. THEY COME IN EITHER WHITE OR DARK BROWN/BLACK AND HAVE A HUGE NUTRITIONAL PROFILE. THEY CONTAIN CALCIUM, MANGANESE, AND PHOSPHORUS, AND ARE PACKED WITH FIBER, PROTEIN, AND HEALTHY OMEGA-3 FATS. THEY ARE BASICALLY TASTELESS SO YOU CAN ADD THEM TO NEARLY ANY KIND OF DISH.

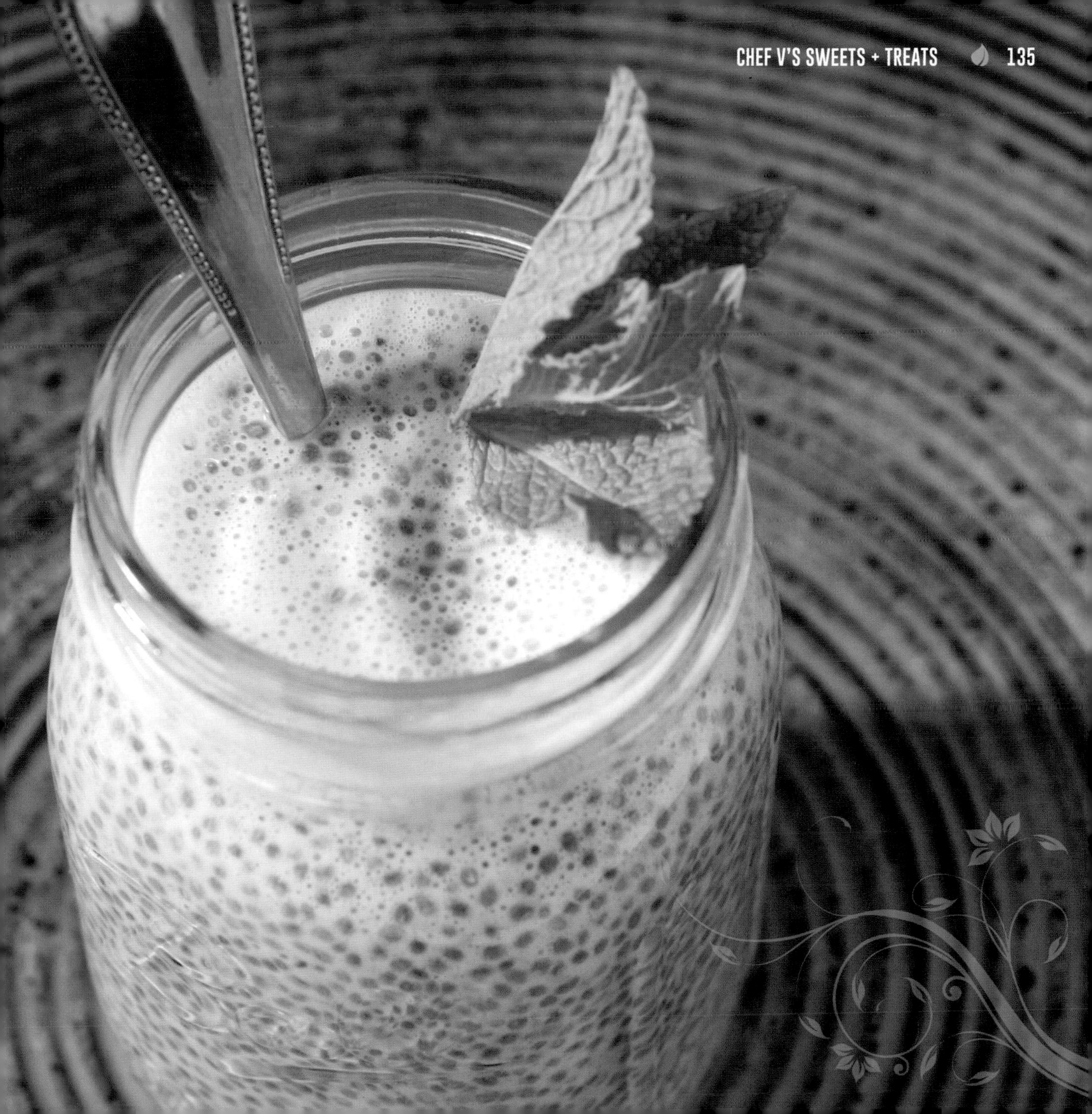

CHOCOLATE AVOCADO MOUSSE
SERVES 1

1 large ripe avocado
3 to 4 tablespoons raw cacao powder
2 tablespoons raw coconut nectar
(I like Coconut Secret®)

OPTIONAL TOPPINGS
Shredded unsweetened coconut
Crushed raw nuts (use your fav!)

Chef V's Tip: This is a delicious dish — chocolate and avocado. What a combo!

Process the avocado, cacao powder, and coconut nectar in a Vitamix until smooth and creamy. Serve it in a dish. For variations or extra flavor, top with shredded coconut or crushed nuts.

CHEF V'S FOOD FACT:
WHEN CACAO BEANS ARE DRIED AT LOW TEMPERATURE, THEY ARE CALLED RAW CACAO BEANS. THEY CAN BE CONSUMED WHOLE, BROKEN INTO PIECES CALLED NIBS, OR GROUND TO PRODUCE RAW COCOA POWDER. THEY ARE RICH IN NATURAL ANTIOXIDANT COMPOUNDS AND HAVE THE HIGHEST PLANT-BASED SOURCE OF IRON. CACAO IS ALSO FULL OF MAGNESIUM — THE MINERAL MOST OFTEN DEFICIENT IN WESTERN DIETS — AND HAS MORE CALCIUM THAN COW'S MILK.

VANILLA 'MILK' SHAKE
SERVES 2

**1 cup Chef V's Raw
Almond Milk**
(*See recipe, page 32*)
or coconut milk
**½ cup cashews, soaked
for 1 hour and drained**
(*See tip, page 35*)
1 cup ice
**1 tablespoon raw
coconut nectar (I like
Coconut Secret®)**
**1 teaspoon pure vanilla
extract**
**1 vanilla bean, scraped,
optional**

Chef V's Tip: Swap the pure vanilla extract for 1 tablespoon raw cacao powder for a yummy chocolate shake!

Process all ingredients in a Vitamix until smooth. Serve immediately.

Ⓥ Ⓡ Ⓟ ⒹⒻ ⒼⒻ ⓀⒻ

For even more vanilla goodness, scrape 1 vanilla bean into the Vitamix and enjoy this flavor-packed dairy-free dessert!

CHEF V'S PRODUCTS + PROGRAMS

ORDER AT CHEFV.COM

I invite you to join me along with the thousands of Chef V customers who experience the benefits of my raw organic green drink, homemade detox soup, and organic cleanses. All of my products are made from locally sourced certified organic ingredients and are delivered to your doorstep free — making it so easy to become a healthier you. Free home delivery includes Chef V's reusable cooler bag.

CHEF V'S ORGANIC GREEN DRINK

Raw and cold blended from 7 super greens and a touch of apple, my nutrient-rich Green Drink is the easiest way to get your daily greens. This low-sugar daily drink cleanses your vital organs and gently rids harmful toxins from the body. My Organic Green Drink will help you burn fat, gain energy, think clearer, and sleep better. Think of it as preventative health care!

CHEF V'S ORGANIC DETOX SOUP

I make my organic detox soup using fresh local ingredients, including organic sweet potato, lemongrass, coconut milk, and a hint of curry. Delicious and filling, my "soup du jour" is a perfect way to help you detoxify the body without going hungry. Serve hot or cold, my soups contain micronutrients proven to help cleanse your liver, prevent cancer, improve digestion, regulate blood sugar, and keep you feeling full!

CHEF V'S ORGANIC DETOX CLEANSES

Available in 3-day, 5-day and 7-day kits, my organic cleanse includes 7 Greens Organic Green Drink, Homemade Detox Soup, Protein Shake Mix, Organic Tea Blend, Shaker Cup, and detailed daily instructions to cleanse your digestive system and rid your body of unwanted toxins and fat without starving the body.

CHEF V'S 21-DAY CHALLENGE

Take your cleansing to the next level. I created my 21-Day Challenge as a powerful way to help my friends break unhealthy habits and lose weight. This program incorporates Chef V's Healthy Routine meal guide, plus two separate 3-Day Cleanse packs over the course of 3 weeks. Follow Chef V's detailed instructions and learn how to eat healthy for life. Get started today and shed unwanted pounds while boosting your energy and confidence!